A Different Kind of Country

By Raymond F. Dasmann

A Different Kind of Country
The Destruction of California
The Last Horizon

A Different Kind
of Country

Raymond F. Dasmann

COLLIER BOOKS

COLLIER-MACMILLAN LTD., LONDON

The Macmillan Company
866 Third Avenue, New York, N.Y. 10022
Collier-Macmillan Canada Ltd., Toronto, Ontario

Library of Congress Catalog Card Number: 68-11193

A Different Kind of Country is published in a
hardcover edition by The Macmillan Company

First Collier Books Edition 1970

ACKNOWLEDGMENTS

The author wishes to express his appreciation for permission to use copy-
righted material to the following: Random House, Inc., for the lines from
Robinson Jeffers' poem "The Purse Seine," reproduced on page 216; Brandt
and Brandt for the lines from Stephen Vincent Benét's poems "Nightmare at
Noon" from *The Selected Works of Stephen Vincent Benét*, Holt, Rinehart
and Winston, copyright 1935 by Stephen Vincent Benét, copyright renewed
© 1963 by Thomas C. Benét, Stephanie B. Mahin and Rachel Benét Lewis,
reproduced on page 1, and "Litany for Dictatorships" from *The Selected
Works of Stephen Vincent Benét*, Holt, Rinehart and Winston, copyright
1940 by Stephen Vincent Benét, reproduced on page 236; John Manifold for
his poem "The Bunyip and the Whistling Kettle," quoted on page 75. The
poem by Montague Grover entitled " 'Loo," quoted on page 164, and
the poem "Where the Dead Men Lie" by Barcroft Henry Boake, quoted on
page 141, appeared in the book *Favourite Australian Poems* published by
Rigby Limited, Adelaide, who inform me that the copyright holder of
the former poem cannot be traced and the latter poem is now in the public
domain.

I also wish to express my appreciation to the National Park Service, the
Department of Housing and Urban Development, the Public Health Service,
the Soil Conservation Service, the Bureau of Reclamation, *The New York
Times*, Reston, James D. Yoakum, Charles F. Yocom, Thane Riney, and the
Swanlund Photo Laboratory for the use of their photographs. Those photo-
graphs not credited are by the author.

Contents

Preface to the Collier Books Edition

❧ THIS BOOK was written during the years between 1965 and 1967 and it reflects the problems and issues of that time. In preparing for a new edition I have felt that I must resist the temptation to revise and update each chapter, since 1970 is not 1967, and one could not write in quite the same way. Nevertheless the problems remain the same and the principles behind them are unchanging. We have made some gains, but the gains are not sufficient.

I was in Paris when we landed our men on the moon and I watched the event on French television. The next day the Russian whose office I shared at UNESCO congratulated me on our American achievement. Since I had opposed the effort from the start, I felt awkward about accepting any credit for it. But like all people who watched this great accomplishment I felt a glow of pride for the demonstration of human courage and technical skill that was involved. I wished only that we could devise some earth spectacular to match our space spectacular, some great project aimed at improving life on earth. I can't take back the words I've written in this book. I believed that our effort at space conquest was misplaced. I still do. When I realize that the entire annual budget for the United Nations is less than 200 million dollars, I resent the billions we squander on rockets and on bombs.

Many of the issues in this book have since been resolved one way or another. We have agreed on a Redwood National Park—not as good a park as some of us had hoped for but better than we had really expected. Now it remains to Congress and the administration to put up the money and the manpower to make it a reality, to build a worthwhile monument to human far-sightedness along the coast of northern California. We have also approved, for better or for worse, a national park in the North Cascades. But the attitudes of the National Park Service toward wilderness remain uncertain and cause me some concern.

Confused thinking about wild lands and wildlife, the foundation stones for diversity, continues. Sentimental feeling for wild animals is offset by revulsion when the same creatures refuse to behave like Walt Disney's little pets. Thus a grizzly bear killed two girls in the Yellowstone wilderness, and now there is talk and action about eliminating the grizzly bear from Yellowstone. That the fault might lie with those who did not inform wilderness travelers of the dangers that should and must be an integral part of wilderness life has not been fully considered. That the Yellowstone wilderness should continue to be dangerous and wild if it is to have any meaning is being ignored. If Yellowstone is to be just another outdoor playground for city folk, let's not call it a national park. National parks have a primary responsibility toward the wild creatures and landscapes within their boundaries. Only secondarily can "parks are for people" be accepted as a slogan for park management.

The great battle for Everglades water was resolved temporarily, in favor of the park. In the course of it the state of Florida as represented by Governor Claude Kirk, and the Central and Southern Florida Flood Control District, came out strongly on the side of conservation. But the water battle did not prove half so difficult as the fight that was to follow it—to prevent the building of a supersonic jet port on the edge of Everglades National Park to serve as a new center for real-estate development and permanent impairment of the ecology of the glades. Surprisingly, however, a new interest in preservation of the environment has swept the state of Florida, and the building of the jet port has also been stopped, if only for the time being. Conservation battles are seldom ended, since developers never give up, but at least for now the news is favorable.

For some of the other issues discussed in this book the news is mixed. The combined efforts of our National Academy of Sciences and the British Royal Society stopped the development of a jet port on Aldabra. The giant tortoises and all of the other different kinds of creatures on this island have been given another lease on life. But in Mexico an expedition by Carl Koford revealed that the last of the grizzly bears had gone from the Sierra del Nido. There may still be a grizzly somewhere in Mexico, but the odds are against it. We can safely add another tier to the monument built to recognize human stupidity and add another name to the list of creatures labeled "extinct."

In 1970 we seem still determined to pursue our course toward a homogenization of the earth under the control of a single dominant human monoculture. The revolt against this process appears to be growing, but those who would protest are so easily led astray and spend their time fighting the wrong battles in the wrong places for dubious causes. It would be easy to build a more grim outlook for the world in 1970 than that which appeared in 1967, but it would be one-sided. There are encouraging signs. UNESCO is taking the lead among United Nations agencies in launching a program aimed at solving some of our major environmental problems. The United Nations General Assembly has called for a Conference on the Human Environment in Stockholm in 1972, intended to launch effective international action. National governments and the press of the leading nations of the world are becoming much more deeply concerned with environmental issues. We still have available to all of us different kinds of country, and perhaps at long last we will take effective action to keep them different. I have stated that the greatest challenge to humanity in what is left of the twentieth century is that of learning how best to maintain human and environmental diversity. It now appears that we may rise to that challenge and may succeed.

RAYMOND F. DASMANN

Washington, D.C.
October 1969

Foreword

THIS BOOK is a plea for diversity—for the preservation of natural diversity and for the creation of man-made diversity—in the hope that the prevailing trend toward uniformity can be arrested and the world kept a fit place for the greatest possible human variety.

One of the more encouraging aspects of our times is that nearly every recommendation made in this book has been adopted, to some degree, even before the book went to press. I have been critical of certain government agencies, but these agencies are, for the most part, at work on correcting the basis for these criticisms. For these advances I can take no credit; the ideas I have expressed and have thought to be original, have also occurred to others. People are thinking about and working on problems of the human environment as never before, and there is great hope that humanity will be able to dig itself out of the predicament into which it has been placed by population growth and advancing technology. On the darker side, the pressures on the environment and the rate of environmental change are greater or more rapid than ever before. The hope for doing the right thing, in time, is therefore diminshed.

I am indebted to Peter Ritner, who conceived the idea, early in 1965, of having me write a book on the American wilderness, and then tolerated the long delay as my wife and I traveled here and there, from Canada to Florida, Europe to Australia, abandoning at least two outlines and early manuscripts until we ended up with a book quite different from what he had suggested in the first place.

I am indebted to Russell Train, president of The Conservation Foundation, who has permitted me to appear irregularly at the office, and even to disappear completely for long periods of time while I worked on this book.

This book has been a joint effort with my wife, Beth. She is responsible for many of the ideas and some of the writing, for the illustrations, and for rejecting some inferior early efforts.

We are both indebted to our daughters, who keep us aware, sometimes uncomfortably aware, of what young people are thinking and doing about the human condition.

RAYMOND F. DASMANN

Washington, D.C.
April 1967

1

A Question of Diversity

Go tell fire it only burns in another country,
Go tell the bombers this is the wrong address,
The hurricane to pass on the other side.
Go tell the earthquake it must not shake the ground.
                                   —Stephen Vincent Benét

❧ S U P P O S E that you lived in Watts. It was not a bad part of Los Angeles once, but that was a long time ago. Now the houses are crowded and public services are, at best, strained. The streets are not safe by night, and the children who play there by day learn to adapt to bullies and to fit in with a gang. Ever present is the atmosphere of despair, disgust and barely suppressed violence. Outside there are other worlds. Some are not far away in distance. You can visit them and see their surface features from the street. There is the surging busyness of down-town Los Angeles, and nearby the tourist-crowded Olvera Street and the old Plaza. There is the luxury of Bel Air, the ostentation of Beverly Hills, the hippy and beatnik world of Sunset Strip, the holiday atmosphere of the beaches. You can visit them, but you do not belong.

On television, radio, the billboards and in newspapers you can get inside these other worlds, see how the people live, see life as viewed from their perspective. You are told daily that these are the American ways of life and you are asked to worry about their problems and concerns. But you are an American and none of these is your way of life. They are there and you want to be a part of them. The knowledge keeps you trying. There are frustrations and times of hopelessness and these lead to trouble and looting and burning because some are impatient, they want their piece of that "good life" now. But even the shoot-ing and the beating and the burning represent hope, the hope of finally being heard, of forcing the power structure to look and listen—a belief that somehow, somebody will build the bridges across from Watts to that land called middle-class America.

But what if there were no outside? The television would each day bring you pictures of life as it goes on in the rest of the world, and all places would be like Watts. The people on the TV screen would be the people that you know, with the same prob-lems, the same despair, but they would live in New York and London, Calcutta and Moscow, Capetown and Peking. Nowhere would anybody be better off. Nothing, anywhere, would be any different. You could protest, but who would listen and who could help? You could riot, and burn, and make things worse, but never better. You could die. That would be different, perhaps.

But soon, we are told, there will be no more Watts, nor anything like Watts left in America. The new technology will shed its benefits on all. Perhaps there will be a model, modern house for each family and all necessities of living in return for some minimum amount of work, or even for none at all. The computers and the electronic industries will handle most of the chores and provide the things you want. You won't need to go shopping, your tele-communication system will provide that what you desire will be brought to you. The children won't need to go to school, they will sit at their home consoles and absorb their programmed education. You will hardly need to travel since you will be able to tune in on any part of the world and see what is going on there. What is going on there? Other people are sitting in their model, modern houses, in their totally planned communities, with all goods and services provided, and they are tuning in on you. You won't want to travel. There will be nothing new to see. There will be no outside. You could protest, but the computers won't listen. You could riot and things would be worse. You could die.

Twenty years ago a man named Aldo Leopold wrote: "There are some who can live without wild things, and some who cannot. These essays are the delights and dilemmas of one who cannot."

Today I must paraphrase Aldo Leopold and say: There are some who believe that technology holds the answers to human problems and there are some who do not. These essays are the dilemmas of one who does not.

John Wilkinson, in a paper called "The quantitative society or what are you to do with Noodle?" has proposed that a refuge be set up for those who wish to reject the automated world of tomorrow and are willing to accept a lower standard of living in consequence. He points out that we refugees in our wilderness ghetto might even build a new Athens. But he warns, if we do it will become of quantitative value and thus subject to takeover by the technological society, which recognizes only quantitative values. Even if we just left things alone, he writes, we would preserve an area of such unique beauty that it too would become of quantitative, speculative value. Consequently there seems

There is still diversity in the world. There are still different kinds of country.

nothing left for us to do but go down fighting, now, while there is still an outside, while there are still places and things that are different.

There is diversity in the world. There are many ways of being rich and ways of being poor.

You could get up before dawn and see the white mist rising from the dambo. Across the grassland the distant trees float free from the ground. You hear the frogs call where the water lies amidst the grasses and the sedges. A village dog stirs from sleep and scratches pensively while considering whether to go first down to drink or to look for some scraps that were not consumed yesterday. The cocks crow a welcome to the sun and hens start to scratch in the dust. A duiker runs from the maize patch into the thornbush scrub. Your neighbors come out and you greet them. There is water to fetch and mealies to prepare and some strips of meat to be grilled over the coals. There is hoeing to be done and fruits to be gathered and more wood needed for the fire. Soon the sun will be warm and children and cicadas will be buzzing. There is the warmth and companionship of the people you know and there are none that you do not know. There is yesterday and tomorrow blended in a continuum of time marked only by births and deaths, marriages and christenings, times of plenty and times of drought, troubles with elephants and sometimes trouble with strangers who come from some place where all things are different.

You could be looking at the far horizon where the low tundra meets the sea and the sky. It is time for sleeping and the sun hangs low in the south. Sled dogs are barking and howling, answering and challenging, from one end of the village to the other. In the distance is a deeper call as a passing wolf seeks to halt this insolent yapping. Today you have fixed your harpoons and finished work on your boat. The ice has broken and the first whales have been seen. Tomorrow you will hunt these baluga, you will see the water churn behind your boat and feel the whip of cold salt spray as you and your fellows strive to be first, the man who killed the first white whale of the season.

You could wake up on your queen-sized foam rubber mattress in your air-conditioned apartment in New York, put on your

There are still choices in ways of living: You could hunt the white whale in the Arctic

Or follow waterbuck in the African savannah

You could fish from a Costa Rican village

Or live in a New York apartment.

Playtex living bra and your nylons and your Lord and Taylor outfit. You plug in your Sunbeam percolator for your morning cup of coffee, pour your frozen Minute Maid orange juice and put your two slices of whole wheat into your General Electric toaster. You regard through the window the faint gleam of the sun as it struggles through the smoke, and put your Metrecal-for-lunch wafers in your handbag. You descend in a noiseless elevator with the silent neighbors you do not know, climb into your new white Cougar and purr out of the driveway to join the traffic crawling at the speed of a slow mule. Lighting a cigarette as defense against exhaust smells, you listen to your car radio tell of war and race troubles, of crime and the highest level of economic activity in the nation's history. Waiting for you at the office today is a pile of papers, different but the same as those that were there yesterday and will be there to-morrow. They tell of transactions in far places for commodities you have never seen, things made of copper perhaps, from Zambia, and iron from the Canadian Arctic.

There are still choices in ways of life. There is still variety in wild places and tame, in human cultures and living places. There are still ways out. This book is about diversity and what has been happening to it. It is written in the belief that the most important thing we can do is to maintain this diversity so that tomorrow there will still be a different kind of country, a different way of life.

Diversity works in many different spheres. Nearly eight years ago my wife and I first became addicted to a form of narcotic known as a "royalty advance." The occasion was the publication of a textbook we had put together, and the amount of money we received, although not large, was adequate to enable me to resign the teaching job that had provided us with a hand-to-mouth existence up to that time, and accept a Fulbright research grant. We packed our goods and chattels, after throwing most of our furniture on the city dump, in an over-age Buick and a "U-Haul" trailer, and drove off down the Redwood Highway on the first leg of a journey to Africa. The decision to resign was not as final as we felt it to be at the time, since we were later to return up the same highway (without the trailer) and take up another teaching post at the same institution. However, in summer, 1959, it seemed to us that we had truly crossed a Rubicon and there was no turning back. Up to then we had led a reasonably normal life, if an artist and a person who studies wild animals and teaches conservation can be considered normal. Nevertheless we had been reasonably representative of professor and faculty wife at a small college and had done most of the things such people do.

What we did not know in summer, 1959, was that we were on the verge of discovering how to slow down the accelerating pace of time. Most people have noticed this distressing property of time, that it passes more swiftly in each succeeding year. I recall 1958 as an unusually short year, blending almost indistinguishably with 1957 and 1956. The year 1959 started off at even greater speed, but in August we stopped it. Between the time when we boarded a jet plane in San Francisco and our first venture into Piccadilly Circus in London, no more than forty-eight hours elapsed. For us, however, an eternity had passed. After three weeks in London, our years in California had faded into the mists of antiquity.

The rate at which time seems to pass depends upon the density of events that transpire and the degree to which they are related to each other. If there is a high density of events, measured in happenings per square hour, and if these bear little relationship to each other, time passes slowly. If each day is like the last and nothing unusual happens, time passes quickly. Young people regard a year as endless because all that happens is new and unrelated to previous experience. This is hardly a new discovery on our part, but it was new to us, and is relevant to this book. The secret of living longer then is in diversity. This can be diversity of experience, doing similar things in different environments, or doing different and unrelated things in the same environment.

Since 1959 I have had unusual opportunities to examine forms of diversity, diversity of environments over the earth, diversity in peoples of the world and their ways of life. I have been able, also, to examine in some parts of the world the trend toward elimination of this variety. Ritchie Calder, writing in the Food and Agricultural Organization journal, has described this trend:

"Science has shrunk the earth in time and distance. Everywhere people are aware of change. I have been most places—in the deserts, in the Arctic, in the jungle, in the high places of the Himalayas and the Andes, and on islands which were once remote. Everywhere, there is this awareness. In the Congo, I have seen radio bulletins picked up by transistor radios and tapped out on talking drums into the swamp forests. In the dyak longhouses of Borneo, youngsters awaiting their pagan initiation into manhood listen to the Beatles. In the Arctic, children who have never seen a wheeled vehicle can identify every aircraft that flies overhead. In the Sahara, the flaming torches of burning exhausts from the oil fields are pillars of smoke by day and pillars of fire by night for the bedouin caravans. On the breathless heights of the altoplano in South America, the disinherited heirs of the Incas watch Disney films. And the jukebox has got to Katmandu."

There is a trend toward uniformity in environment, people and ways of life over all the earth. This trend is in the long run inimical to life, including human life. It is therefore a concern of this book. It will do us little good to conquer nature or even pacify mankind if the world we create is bland and uniform, one where life passes quickly because nothing new can happen again anywhere.

There are still many ways of earning a living in the world, and one of them is the way I have ventured on, that of an ecologist. Ecology, like other sciences, offers a variety of careers to its followers. You could become a specialist and spend your time in field or laboratory pursuing research into some new secret of nature: how nutrients move from soil to animals; why redwood seedlings survive poorly in undisturbed forests; why wren-tits are not more abundant; or how you can treat a pasture to make it feed two cows instead of one. Such research can absorb you completely and keep you unaware of other events in the world. You could, however, devote your time to teaching and become wrapped up with the techniques of this profession, with the education of new generations or the administration of colleges and universities. This could also consume most of your time and interest. However, you could decide to consider the broader implications of ecological knowledge in relation to man and his world. If you take this latter course you will never again be entirely at ease. In today's world ecology can be an uncomfortable discipline. The questions it will raise may put you out of step with your fellow men.

We live in a country that leads the world in economic production. We have an unprecedented standard of material well-being. We hear often that tomorrow's problem will be what to do with our leisure and that seems small cause for worry. Yet recently I checked with many of the leaders in my own field and related areas concerned with man and his environment. Everywhere the same storm warnings were flying, the same belief that we are heading into a growing crisis. At best I found hope that we would change our course. More commonly I found the feeling that if luck held we would get by with some minor catastrophes, affecting the tens of millions rather than the hundreds of millions. If our luck still held we would then learn the lessons needed for survival.

Why is there this discrepancy between our official attitude of well-being and optimism and this minority report from well-qualified experts. Perhaps the answer lies in the ecological viewpoint shared by all whom I consulted. Ecology is concerned with inter-relationships. These are out of balance.

Ecology is the study of living things in relation to each other and to their environment. Particularly it is the study of populations and communities and the ways these interact. It is by necessity an integrating science, depending on other fields for information and principles that can be applied to the relationships of populations and communities. Ecologists are not all-purpose, all-around scientists. There are no such beings. They need, however, a sufficient grasp of other sciences to know which expert to turn to. An ecologist may focus his interest on a study of a wild population in some remote area. He may also study domesticated plants or animals. He may use a laboratory culture of protozoans as his field for study. He may equally well study the human situation. Since man exists only in relationship to other men, other animals, plants and the physical environment of the earth, ecology forms one means for exploring man's role on

Ecologists can be concerned with populations of deer or with air pollution in cities. Both represent aspects of ecological systems. (*Photograph below, courtesy of United States Public Health Service*)

earth. Ecology is not conservation. It can, however, provide a scientific background on which the social attitudes of conservation can be based.

In the days before I started to concern myself with the ecological implications of man's activities, I lived a fairly simple and happy life studying the ecology of deer. I was a fairly capable deer watcher and deer trapper. I spent many long days on hilltops in central California with field glasses and notebook, watching and recording the activities of a population of deer that inhabited the wild chaparral country. In time I knew most of the animals in the area and could assign a name or number to many of them. It became possible to know how they would react, what they ate, where they sought shelter and the details of their family lives. However, before the study was complete it was necessary to seek the advice, oral or published, of geologists, hydrologists, soil scientists, meteorologists, biochemists, pathologists, endocrinologists, embryologists and many other scientists as well as to concern ourselves with psychology, sociology, history, economics, political science and geography. All of these contributed to understanding the ecology of black-tailed deer in California's chaparral. Our understanding is far from complete.

The area with which ecology is concerned is the biosphere. This is the thin mantle of air, water, soil and rock that covers the surface of the earth and the living things that dwell in it. Inward, toward the earth's interior, there is no life. Outward, beyond the atmosphere, we have yet to find life. If we discover life outside the earth the domain of ecology will be extended. For now the biosphere is enough to worry about. Its future seems precarious. Since we are all part of it and depend on it for existence, our own future seems none too secure.

Within the biosphere ecology is concerned with ecological systems, ecosystems. These are the various living communities with all of their diverse species and their non-living physical environment. A pond is an example of a fairly discrete ecosystem; so is an island. Most ecosystems have somewhat arbitrary boundaries since in nature few things are as clearly defined as they are on maps. Modification of any part of an ecosystem affects the entire system. Cutting the trees in a forest affects not just the trees but all the plants, all the animals, the micro-climate, the soil and so on. A realization of the inter-relationships within an ecosystem is essential for man's continued occupancy on earth. We cannot go on polluting our air or our rivers without affecting all life. We cannot, for example, continue with impunity to increase the carbon dioxide content of the atmosphere at the rate

The biosphere in which man has always lived has been characterized by biological and geological variety. Such diversity is unusual in the history of the planet; over most of geological time a greater uniformity prevailed.

it has been increased over the past fifty years. The consequences of such interference with the biosphere, the world ecosystem, would be disastrous climatic change. Diversity has always characterized the biosphere to which man belonged. We will consider how this came to be later, since the world has not always been a highly diverse place. Man's world, however, has been. In living systems, complexity brings stability and ability to withstand change. The future survival of man may well depend on the continuing complexity of the biosphere.

It is worthwhile considering for a time that portion of the biosphere that we call the United States. Our history in this land and our attitudes toward it explain the trend within it away from diversity, toward uniformity of environment and culture.

The words of Benjamin Franklin "They that can give up essential liberty to obtain a little temporary safety deserve neither liberty nor safety" have often been quoted in many contexts, usually associated with a waving of the flag. They are nevertheless relevant here. We have long been engaged in a process of sacrificing essential liberty, the freedom for future change; essential diversity, the environment that would support such change; and essential cultural variety, the knowledge to implement such change in order to obtain a little security through increased material well-being. The loss of liberty and variety is gradual. Each step is hardly noticed, since it is measured against the immediate past and weighed against some immediate material gain. But each episode brings an almost irreversible change. We lose a way of life perhaps or an environment that made that way of life possible. Sometimes it is an irreplaceable thing that we sacrifice, a wild species perhaps; sometimes it is a way of doing things that could be regained if we had the will. With all of the space that any people could require in our American continent, with room and resources to support a hundred different ways of living, we give up each in turn. Diversity dwindles, choices narrow, and we find ourselves moving toward a technologically driven, computer-directed culture that we cannot abandon without disaster.

In the America that we inherited the many environments supported many kinds of people. Over the millennia, primitive peoples living in isolated places had devised ways of living with the land. In places they produced strange flowerings of civilization—from the peaceful ways of the pueblos to the fear-ridden violence of the Aztec lands. But none of their ways were understandable to the invaders who came over the Atlantic. Driven by ideals or by avarice, the men from Europe sought not to understand but to subdue the New World and its peoples, to build in it another England or another Spain.

It is easier perhaps for westerners to understand some of the balance of losses and gains since they are closer to their country's past. In the East many episodes are so far back in time that even the scar tissues have disappeared. In the West, however, there are some still alive who were around when the horsemen of Geronimo came down from the Arizona crags, forced at last to surrender. People heralded the finish of the last of the unsubdued Indians and the end of a long and vicious struggle. It was a decade earlier that the Modocs made their last desperate stand in the lava rocks of northern California, and earlier still that the Nez Perce in the Idaho country staged their epochal long march and met their final defeat. Only a few know of their Chief Joseph's statement of a lost cause: "my heart is sick and sad. From where the sun now stands I will fight no more, forever." And they fought no more forever, the Nez Perce and the Sioux, the Blackfeet and Cheyenne, the Crow and the Apache. It matters no longer whether they were right or wrong. The land was theirs but they could not hold it. It matters that when they were crushed something vital was crushed with them, not to be regained. The blue smoke of their campfires vanished from the prairie skies and America gained a "little safety." Only a freedom was gone, a freedom to be different.

Geronimo had surrendered, but the Old West was still alive. The men who fought the Indians were themselves a tough breed, in a rough land, careless of security. Teddy Roosevelt was to search among them for men to storm San Juan Hill, others lived to chase the Moros in the jungles of the Philippines or to drift to South Africa to try their skills against the Zulu. Quite a number were still alive when the finish was written forever to their kind of fighting and their way of life by a world that had scant room for heroes in the muddy trenches of France.

The blue coats of the cavalry vanished, but the West was still open and many of the old ways hung on. A boy could leave the city and go out with his saddle to wrangle horses for a cow outfit in Nevada. He could ride the old ranges, talk the old talk, visit the cow towns. Old Texas and the plunging herds of the Chisholm Trail could seem to be just over the far horizon. But the wiser heads were packing their gear and heading for the Argentine or Australia, where the future could be staved off for a while longer. Others stayed to watch the last big roundup on the open range, and lived to calculate neat balances of beef losses and beef gains on managed lands that were nowhere any longer to be free.

In the mountains of the Southwest there was wilderness, visited perhaps but not yet changed by man. The wilderness was rocks and soil and untouched vegetation. Most of all the wilderness was the animal life. Here the lonely camper could hear the gray wolf howl, and the unwary traveler might come face up to a grizzly bear. But the trail herds were settling all over the West. Herders with rifles and government men with steel traps and poison baits came onto the scene, and then there was the last lobo, and the last bear. The world was safe for sheep and for memories of days when the mountains still had the soul of a grizzly, and the night winds brought a tickling along the spine of the watcher by the campfire.

There are still those around who can remember when there were blank spots on the American map, places not surveyed and flown over only by birds. But we passed another point of no return when the last of these was traveled. The old wilderness wanderers had that satisfaction of being the first to climb a mountain, sail a river, survey a township. But we were a restless, inquisitive people who could not quit until we had ferreted out all of geography's larger secrets. We could not leave a desert unvisited, or a lake without a name. An unclimbed mountain was an irresistible challenge. We could not bear to leave places marked "unexplored," unmapped and unnamed.

Once the wilderness was simply the country beyond, somewhat forbidding, largely unknown, entirely undeveloped. (*Photograph by George Grant, courtesy of National Park Service*)

Once the wilderness was simply the country beyond, somewhat forbidding, largely unknown, entirely undeveloped. Its essential quality was best identified by Aldo Leopold, who fought to save it, in a quotation from Robert Service: "where nameless men by nameless rivers wander, and in strange places die strange deaths, alone." That wilderness vanished from North America, its passing unnoticed at the time. It cannot be recalled. The little remnants of undisturbed land that remain give us a chance to wander for a while and dream a little, but they are not the old reality. In the Arctic and some tropical places, more elements of the old wilderness persist. The rivers have names and the men pack identity cards, but there are still the wolves and the bears, or the jaguars. The opportunity to get lost in remote places and die strange deaths alone still persists. There may still be wild Indians who can assist in the process.

Wilderness is a word that has developed special meanings in these days when all lands are mapped and measured. Sometimes I wonder if our final act of wilderness destruction did not lie in designating formal wilderness areas for preservation. In

The demand for wild country grows, the supply is diminishing.

defining the boundaries, writing the rules and publicizing the results, did we not remove the last magic and make all realize that the remote and unknown was now available to all?

I like the term "wild land" because it does not have the modern implications of wilderness. There are wild places on the globe that have been much modified by human action, where the vegetation and animal life have changed from more primitive days, and are yet more wild than any United States wilderness. Dangerous animals and not-too-friendly people add touches to some thoroughly mapped areas in other countries that give the civilized visitor a kinship with Kit Carson, David Livingstone or Alexander von Humboldt that is forever denied him in modern America.

Today wild lands may be in greater danger than we realize because of confused thinking and conflicting attitudes toward them. Unless we straighten out our feelings and emotions about these places, clarify our thinking about what we hope to preserve and why, the men with slide-rule minds and computerized souls may well manage them out of existence, using our own confused reasoning for their justification. I heard a man recently, a supposed believer in wilderness, justify the creation of a national park in a very wild area by saying "it will pick up some of the half million Americans who now head north to Canada each summer." Perhaps it will, but by what miracle will it then still be wild?

We are a city people today, born and reared in urban ways, remote from both farms and wild country. Yet our very urbanization brings a greater demand for nature and wild land. More of us live in cities than ever before, and never before has there been such a pressure of people upon every wild place in America. Wild lands are essential to our spirit and our personal freedom. They are part of the remaining heritage of diversity that we cannot afford to lose. I hope to convince unbelievers, who are legion, of this importance so that these lands and the values associated with them shall not join the list of what has forever gone. But there is a danger in doing this if every new convert wishes to go and worship at some wilderness shrine. The greatest danger to wild lands now is the pressure of people, and perhaps we must ask even those who love the wilderness most to touch it but seldom, and lightly. It may well have been better off when nobody cared.

We have reached a point in time where it is essential to recognize that we are being misled. We are misinformed by those in whom we have placed too much trust, the spokesmen for technology and the government leaders who consult them as their sole oracle. Consequently we are wasting our strength and resources in fields remote from our own needs. At a time when we must learn how to get along with each other, and even how to achieve an integration of our own inner selves, we are sending rockets to the moon and building more capable instruments for our own destruction. Lewis Mumford has compared our rockets to the Egyptian pyramids, both built at enormous cost for no useful purpose save perhaps our own self-glorification. Our entire pursuit bears resemblance to the old northwest Indian custom of potlatching in which each group destroyed its own wealth in a spirit of competition with its rivals.

At a time when the preservation of the human environment, with all of its diversity, is our most important need, we give full support only to a process of technological change that will erode variety in both nature and man.

We should be able to rejoice at the conquest of outer space, at man's new venture into the unknown, were it not given precedence above more urgent human problems, those of hunger, misery and lack of opportunity. A Negro woman interviewed on television in relation to the abandonment of a poverty relief program stated it very well: "We don't want to go to the moon hungry." I don't know who will first set foot on the moon. I know that he will be poorly informed about the realities of the earth from which he came, poorly equipped to deal with its ecological or social complexities. This is the irony. He will find no answers to human problems in outer space and he will return to a world destroying itself.

Despite all talk of what our technology *could* accomplish, we are not today on the verge of prosperity and happiness for all.

The rocks here are some of
the oldest in the Park. They are
part of the Hector formation
and were deposited as
sediments in Precambrian times
over 500 million years ago

People get everywhere.

Instead we have the recent words of the director of the Food and Agricultural Organization of the United Nations: "The outlook is alarming. In some of the most heavily populated areas the outbreak of serious famines within the next five to ten years cannot be excluded. And if food output everywhere just kept pace with population growth at the present level of consumption, by the end of this century the number of people who would be subject to hunger and malnutrition would be double what it is today." A food scientist, Georg Borgstrom, writes: "Man threatens to deprive himself of a future by refusing to recognize his predicament. Insanely we try to talk ourselves out of reality. We refuse to acknowledge the rising human tidal wave."

Considering only the three threats of war, population and pollution, one could make a case to show that we are nearing the end of what we may look back on as a brief golden age, as the people of the Dark Ages once looked back at the glories of ancient Rome. Since I am by nature optimistic, I believe we will make the necessary changes, and that despite some catastrophes, we will find our way out. There is evidence that some people are trying as never before to find this way. Most of them are young people. This is their weakness and their strength.

There are times in history when individuals become of supreme importance. This is one of them. No one can predict what tomorrow will be with any degree of confidence. We all try since we must make plans and continue to live, but we do not know when somebody in some far off land will make a decision that will change the course for mankind. We do not live in a time of crisis but of multiple, recurrent crises, all taking place at once. Sometimes, overwhelmed by the omnipresence of an all-pervading technology, and aware of the existence of more than three billion people on earth, we feel that the individual counts for little. Yet it remains that certain individuals count for a great deal, if their names happen to be Mao Tse-tung, Ho Chi Minh, Lyndon B. Johnson, Charles de Gaulle, or others who are featured in the news. We do not know today what trends in our society will prove most important for tomorrow, what individuals unknown to us now may shape the future. Lewis Mumford has

There are times in history when individuals become of supreme importance. This is one of them.

pointed out that nobody in the first century A.D. knew that the scattered groups who called themselves Christian would ever have importance in a world dominated by Imperial Rome. These few had no power or importance except that they were bearing the ideas that would shape the future when Rome collapsed in ruins. Writing of our present times Carl Jung has said: "As at the beginning of the Christian Era, so again today we are faced with the problem of the moral backwardness which has failed to keep pace with our scientific, technical and social developments. So much is at stake and so much depends on the psychological constitution of modern man. Is he capable of resisting the temptation to use his power for the purpose of staging a world conflagration? Is he conscious of the path he is treading, and what the conclusions are that must be drawn from the present world situation and his own psychic situation? Does he know that he is on the point of losing the life-preserving myth of the inner man which Christianity has treasured up for him? Does he realize what lies in store should this catastrophe ever befall him? Is he even capable at all of realizing that this would be a catastrophe? And finally, does the individual know that *he* is the makeweight that tips the scales?"

Today each of us has a choice. He can remain a statistic, one of the three-plus billion, or he can take responsibility for his world and attempt to influence its direction. If he does he may be the individual at the right time at the right place with the right lever who will shift the world. This is the challenge of an age of revolution.

2

The Stored Wealth of Nature

For his own security, as well as to ensure the proper worship of his god, the machine, post-historic man must remove any memory of things that are wild and untamable, pied and dappled, unique and precious; mountains one might be tempted to climb, deserts where one might seek solitude and inner peace, jungles whose living creatures would remind some surviving, unaltered human explorer of nature's original prodigality in creating a grand diversity of habitat and habits of life out of the primeval rock and protoplasm with which she began.

—Lewis Mumford

THE world in which man has lived has been character- ized by diversity. The great variety of environments and of living creatures available to man, however, are a relatively recent and uncommon phenomena in the long history of earth. Man has always lived in a time of revolution. It may be that a species such as *Homo sapiens* could only have come into existence at such a time. Perhaps in a quieter world we would lose those qualities that we now include in the definition of human. The revolution that I refer to here is geological in nature, but the implications for other areas are obvious.

For our own glorification we prefer to describe the present time in earth's history as the Recent Epoch. It is, however, part of the Pleistocene, the ice ages of earth, an epoch unlike any that occurred on earth before. We do not know for sure whether we are living in a period of ice retreat or ice advance. We know that some twelve thousand years ago much of the area that now supports life in the northern continents was covered by glaciers. We know these melted away and have since returned to occupy the Antarctic and Greenland and higher mountains elsewhere. We are inclined to believe that the future will depend on what happens to our atmosphere. If we continue to burn fossil fuels at accelerating rates we may build up the carbon dioxide content of this atmosphere to a point where a marked "green- house effect" sets in and the earth's heat is trapped to a greater degree by the atmosphere. Sufficient warming could occur to melt the remaining glaciers quite rapidly. The end result could be a balmy, subtropical climate over much of the temperate zone. Unfortunately we would not appreciate this as fully as we might be expected to, since sea levels would be raised by the melting ice and most of our seacoast areas, including our largest cities, would be submerged.

Ice ages are unusual in the billions of years of earth history. They are associated with such unusual features on the earth's surface as high mountains, deserts, elevated plateaus, deep canyons, and the varied vegetation and animal life that are asso- ciated with such geological features. Man came into existence as

Glaciers have returned to the high mountains. The Columbian ice fields.

a species during the Pleistocene. His ancestors lived in a much less varied world. Our social and cultural evolution has been encouraged by the unusual variety of geological and biological environments that characterize the ice age world.

What can be considered a normal condition for the earth, a condition toward which the forces of gravity, blowing winds and moving waters tend to drive it, is a world in which there are no high mountains or great differences in surface elevation. The oceans would be more extensive and the continents uniform and of low relief blending with inland seas. There would be no areas of extreme cold, and consequently those forms of life that now exist in temperate regions would be found in polar areas. No areas would be arid. Day would follow day with little change in weather. Seasons would hardly exist. One place would be much like another with only a gradual blending over hundreds or thousands of miles from forms of life that prefer the warmer tropics to those that survive best at the cooler poles; from those that prefer submergence in water to those that do best on drier ground.

This kind of world is the one in which the great reptiles, the dinosaurs, lived, and, earlier in time, the large amphibians. Still earlier it was the world available when life first came out of the ancient seas and moved onto the land. It was a world without flowering plants, without grasslands or broad-leaved forests, without birds or mammals, and without anything resembling intelligence, or man. So at least has been deduced from the geological and biological records left from this past.

Evolution proceeds through environmental challenge. A stable environment provides a continuing home to those creatures already established. A changing environment provides opportunity to those that are different or can change to suit the circumstances. The great period of dominance of amphibians, the Paleozoic, came to an end with a period of change, the Permian, over two hundred million years ago. Mountains were uplifted at this time and with them came climatic extremes of dryness and cold. Glaciers formed, but oddly, their scars are found only in southern hemisphere continents in areas where glaciation would not be expected were the present ice age to turn colder. They suggest that the continents were differently located. The environmental extremes of this glacial age both disturbed the long-prevailing equilibrium under which the old amphibians had thrived and gave opportunity to those creatures better adapted to uplands and dryness—the reptiles.

Around sixty million years ago the world that the giant reptiles had found salubrious also came to an end as mountains and cold weather, dry heat and drought once again began to appear on the earth's surface. During the millions of years of the Mesozoic the world that the reptiles occupied had lapsed again into its more normal state of warmth, dampness and uniformity. The reptiles that evolved in this world perhaps lost the capacity

Man and volcanoes, storms and ice floes, droughts and floods go together. Mount Katmai, Alaska. (*Photograph courtesy of National Park Service*)

to adapt to change, and so, like the amphibians before them, they vanished. Small, warm-blooded creatures, the birds and mammals, that seemed insignificant in a world dominated by *Tyrannosaurus* and other, more peaceable, dinosaurs, found opportunity in the new period of revolution. They were to dominate in a world made green by deciduous forests, flowering herbs and grasses that waved in the wind.

But once again the world returned toward a more normal climate and terrain. Vegetation and animal life spread poleward. Giant mammals evolved to feed on lush vegetation in areas now desert. Again, however, change appeared and the extremes of the Pleistocene arrived on earth. Glaciers sculptured the world man was to occupy. Man and volcanoes, storms and ice floes, droughts and floods go together. For millions of years the forces that drive and shape living organisms had been working to produce a maximum diversity of life: creatures that could survive in a desert or live at the edge of an ice cap or adapt to the intense competition of life in a tropical forest. This diversity flowered as part of the biosphere in which man found his home.

It is impossible to trace in detail the evolution of human variety since the records have yet to be found. We know that the existence of natural variety favored human diversity. The early home of mankind appears to have been in the dry tropics in a forest edge environment, but people spread widely over the earth. Groups of people occupying different environments, isolated from one another, developed the characteristics that differentiate the races of man today. Within these broad racial groups people were to evolve who could adapt to life in the humid, tropical forests as the pygmies have done. Men learned to hunt game and adjust to the ways of arid deserts as the Bushmen and the aborigines of Australia have managed. On the edges of tropical forests, perhaps, people learned the arts of agriculture. In more arid lands of Asia and Africa they domesticated the herding animals and some, such as the Bedouins and Tuaregs, became desert herders. Eskimos evolved who could survive well in the land of seals and caribou in the far Arctic. Others took to the mountains and learned to live in the thin air and biting cold of the high Andes or Himalayas. In the flood plains of the desert rivers they learned the arts that led to civilization. All the varieties of human physical types, the even greater numbers of separate human cultures, owe their differences, their characteristics and their skills to the varied environments that they occupied, that offered different challenges and different rewards for human effort. The diversity of races and peoples, cultures and customs permitted the survival and spread of man. This human diversity may well be our most valuable heritage from the past. It may be the only long-term hope for survival into the future.

To consider the characteristics of diversity it is best to have a look at the natural world, relatively unmodified by man, and then to consider how human activities tend to affect it. If you were to roam over the globe looking for the place most favorable to the greatest variety of animal and plant life, you would end up, without question, somewhere within the humid tropics, in a biotic community known as tropical rain forest. Here the conditions for life are most nearly ideal. There are no extremes of climate and winter does not come. In the rain forest of New Guinea, for example, temperatures are in the eighties in the daytime, dropping to the seventies at night. There is no dry season in the sense of a time when the ground dries out and plant growth ceases for lack of moisture. There may be periods when more rain falls and periods when the rainfall is less, but at Singapore, for example, at least six inches of rain falls in every month. In consequence there are no growing seasons as such, no season of flowering, no leaf-drop season, no period of inactivity. There is no breeding season among animals, and young are produced throughout the year. Each species may follow its own internal rhythm, but for the community as a whole there are always flowers and fruit to be found and young animals being born.

The most biologically diverse environment on earth: tropical rain forest.

This rain forest is characteristic of tropical lowlands. If you climb tropical mountains, conditions change, and if you go high enough you encounter cold, snow and rigorous conditions for life. On tropical islands the leeward slopes often will be dry and with less complex vegetation. Mountain ranges on continents can also create rain shadows where drought-adapted vegetation grows. Lowland rain-forest climates are not widespread: the Amazon Basin and some surrounding country, the lowlands of Central America, the Congo Basin, Southeast Asia and tropical islands are the areas where the optimum conditions for living things will be found.

If the tropical lowlands with their rain forests are considered as the apex of a right angle triangle, extremes that are unfavorable to life will be found by following out either side of the triangle. If one side represents a gradient of moisture, that corner of the triangle would be occupied by tropical deserts such as are found in coastal Peru. Moving out along that side from rain forest to desert you would also move from diversity to simplicity, from highly complex life to conditions that were much less varied. If the other side of the triangle represents temperature, its far corner will be occupied by areas too cold to support any but a few hardy, adaptable species, such as Antarctica or Greenland, or, if we move altitudinally instead of latitudinally, by the nearly lifeless, cold elevations of such high mountains as Kilimanjaro or Chimborazo.

The comparisons between the variety of living things in the humid tropics and in other areas where climate is less favorable to life are most convincing. In the Americas, for example, Labrador has 81 species of breeding birds, New York State supports 195, Guatemala 469, Panama 1,100 and equatorial Colombia 1,395. The entire continent of Europe has only slightly more than 250 species of breeding land birds. There are well over 2,000 species of dragonflies in the tropics and subtropics, only 1,000 or less in the rest of the world; 3,000 species of ants and termites are tropical compared to slightly over 1,000 species in all the non-tropical world.

With the enormous number of species in the humid tropics there is intense competition for places in the environment or ecological niches. This restricts the number of individuals of a single species compared to what one would find in the temperate zone. Hence tropical forestry runs into difficulties, because timber trees of value are usually widely scattered in dense rain forests. One may find only a single mahogany tree in one location surrounded by dozens of trees of other species. It is difficult to carry out a program of careful use and management of forests where the more valuable trees must be searched out in their widely scattered hiding places. In the temperate zone, by contrast, you may travel over miles of mountain forest and encounter no large tree but ponderosa pine; in the subarctic coniferous forest, two species, white spruce and black spruce, may be the only dominants over many square miles. But in Malaya there are 5,000 species of plants, of which 2,000 are trees, and you may find 60 species in a plot no bigger than a hectare.

There are exceptions to these general rules. Islands and small isolated continents, such as Australia, will have less variety, fewer species, than the larger continents. The large mammals, the big game of Africa, for example, reach their greatest diversity and abundance away from the rain forests in the subhumid and semi-arid tropics. For the large grazing and browsing animals the

The abundance of large mammals in the dry tropics of Africa is unmatched elsewhere in the world.

vegetation of the drier tropics offers a more suitable diet. Nevertheless the general rule about tropics versus temperate regions applies equally to subhumid and semi-arid zones. The massive abundance and variety of big game in Africa was approached in historical times only in the similar climate and habitat of tropical Asia.

The significance of this diversity may be considered from many points of view. Thus the tropics represent a vast reservoir of genetic material that we have only begun to examine and make use of. It has already contributed drugs and medicines, many of our domesticated food and fiber plants, some of our domesticated animals, valuable timbers and so forth. Each year sees some new addition to our catalogue of useful species as we explore the values of this tropical material. We cannot foresee what contributions may come in the future or what keys to human welfare may be found in this biological storehouse. We know that for practical reasons alone we cannot afford to lose it. Its value to the human spirit, less obvious but perhaps more important in the long run, is another consideration.

Looked at from another viewpoint, the diversity of the tropics offers clues to proper management of lands and people elsewhere. Biological diversity is associated with stability and adaptability. The great variety of species present in tropical areas provides for a system of buffers, of checks and balances, that regulates the abundance or scarcity of any species. Competition for space is intense so that only the species best adapted to a particular site will be able to hold its place there. This in itself acts to prevent any one species from becoming excessively numerous. There is also a remarkable degree of interaction between species, particularly between plants and animals. In temperate zones it is possible for plant ecology to operate almost as an independent study from animal ecology. In the tropics this is hardly possible since plants more obviously depend on animals.

The tropics support the greatest variety of nectar-feeding birds that depend on plant flowers for their sustenance. The plants, however, make use of the birds for pollination. A particular species of plant will have a flower adapted to attract and accommodate a particular kind of bird, which will then pick up

Simplified biotic communities are found in the more extreme environments: the cold Arctic or the arid deserts.

pollen and transfer it, not at random, but to a flower of the same species. Insects and flowers show an even greater degree of specialized adaptation to each other. Thus one tropical orchid has a flower that resembles in markings a female wasp of a particular species. Male wasps of that species are attracted by the flower and the female wasps seek out the flower to find the males. In the process they transfer pollen from one flower of that species to another. If one recalls that individuals of any plant species are likely to be widely scattered in the rain forest, the importance of these specially adapted birds or insects can be realized. The species could hardly survive if it relied on wind or chance to carry pollen from one plant to another. This intricate relationship between species is in itself a check against the increase of a single species to any high level of abundance.

Overabundance in any species of animal is also limited by the great variety of things—predators, parasites, diseases—that prey on it. Any excessive numbers of young animals that are produced soon will be picked off by one or another enemy. On the other hand, when a species becomes scarce, its enemies are more likely to seek some alternate prey which will support them until the first species becomes more available again. Thus either increase or decline tends to be held within a narrow range. One may be forgiven for doubting this when he is overwhelmed by swarms of mosquitoes, or bitten by leaf-cutting ants. The average visitor from the temperate zone may feel that there is always an overabundance of tropical insects; however, he is seeing only a normal level of tropical profusion.

One who is accustomed to colder regions will usually be amazed at the speed with which bare areas are occupied in the tropics. A clearing in the forest does not stay clear long. A volcanic lava flow is quickly colonized and soon supports a thriving community. Barrenness in the tropics is usually associated only with the effects of civilized man. Only he seems able to create and maintain lifelessness in an environment where some species is always waiting to colonize any vacant space.

In contrast with the tropics, when one reaches the cold Arctic regions of the earth he may believe that there is no such thing as stability among animal populations. There are apparently no lemmings, or there are lemmings swarming everywhere; there are no white foxes or white foxes regard you from every hummock. In the subarctic forests snowshoe hares will overrun the countryside and then decline to absolute scarcity, leaving the lynxes that feed on them stalking the woods, hungry and gaunt, in search of any alternate prey. The exceptions appear to be the larger mammals, such as polar bears and muskoxen, which have relatively low breeding rates. These may follow some longer cycle of abundance and scarcity but it is not evident.

If one travels to the dry extremes of the earth one finds a similar boom-and-bust cycle. There are jackrabbits everywhere in the desert one year and the next year none are seen. Locusts swarm in plagues or locusts are scarce. All these cycles or irruptions in the numbers of animals appear related to the extremes of climate and to the relative simplicity of the ecosystems. There are no great numbers of species of predators nor of prey on which to feed. Lemmings in the Arctic may be almost the sole prey for weasels, foxes, hawks and owls, but when the lemmings decrease in numbers there are no other species that can support these predators. They must move out, or starve, and thus will not be present in sufficient abundance to hold down the next upswing of the lemming cycle. The plants are also less varied. No alternate range of suitable food plants exists for the caribou to turn to when it overgrazes the lichens that grow in the taiga.

Insect pests and disease organisms also fluctuate. Rabies, distemper or mange can sweep quickly through Arctic wolves and foxes leaving them decimated. For years afterward there will be no similar outbreak. An insect such as the spruce budworm or the larch sawfly can sweep through and damage or kill vast areas of forest. Climate, however, acts as a major control on all species, particularly in arid regions where droughts can last for years and cause a decrease in all forms of life. A sudden wet year can, in turn, allow everything to increase to peaks of abundance. Even in the absence of effective predators, insects cannot go on at pest levels year after year. The cold or dry year, the unusual season, will kill them off.

Man has built his civilization and maintains it by tapping the stored riches of nature and by modifying natural environments. Obviously we could not feed our present populations by harvesting the seeds of wild grasses, garnering fruits from natural forests, hunting wild game. We have progressed by taking the energy that flows in diverse pathways through natural communities and channeling it into the calories of our food plants and animals— the wheat, rice and corn; the beef cattle and lambs. In most areas this involves simplifying natural ecosystems. We remove all of the many wild species of plants that once grew in the prairies and substitute for them the one species, corn. The energy that once flowed through all the wild plants into mice and rabbits, weasels and foxes, hawks and owls is channeled in a pathway that leads from corn to man, or corn to hog to man. Thus we achieve the abundance of food needed for two hundred million Americans and the starving millions in other lands. But we do this at a cost and a risk.

In simplifying a diversified ecosystem we set in motion the forces that operate normally in the more simple systems of Arctic or desert—instability, boom-and-bust, peaks and troughs of populations. The wheat may do well in western Kansas for many years, but then drought comes, the wheat fails, and there are no buffalo or grama grass to hold the soil. We have a dust bowl. Corn does well in Illinois, but then climate favors chinch bugs and the corn crop is decimated. Wheat does well in the Dakotas, but provides a home for smuts or rusts that attack wheat, and farmers go broke. Soils, devoid of the biological balance that once built them and sustained them, become compacted or exhausted of fertility. Such conditions, in our history, reached a peak in the 1930s, a period that also marked the end of completely destructive exploitation of our lands. Since then we have become skillful at substituting man-made for natural processes. Fertilizers, insecticides, herbicides, fungicides, crop rotations, mulchings, all of the agricultural skills that we can devise have been brought to work on the land. We still have failures, we still make mistakes, but generally we have devised a satisfactory, artificial substitute for natural processes and in some ways we have improved on natural systems. Crop surpluses, not scarcity, have become our major problem. But in substituting for nature we have to go all the way, we must substitute for natural complexity equally complex human activity. The price for continued success is continued vigilance.

The extreme of environmental simplification comes with the one-crop system known as monoculture. A monoculture can be highly productive, but it is also highly risky. One of the textbook examples of such success and failure is provided by Ireland's experience with the potato. Before the potato arrived from the New World, Ireland had diversified farming that emphasized production of cereal grains. Such agriculture supported a population that is estimated to have been around one million in 1670. The potato was adapted to Ireland's soil and climate, and the Irish adapted to the potato. Its abundant yield permitted subdivision of the Irish farms into small plots, each of which could produce enough to support a family. This in turn permitted early marriages and encouraged high fertility. In the great potato boom the number of Irish increased, to three million in 1760, seven million by 1821 and then to over eight million by 1845.

Every species finds its own enemies sooner or later. In 1846 the troubles began. A fungus disease, the potato blight, hit the Irish crops. During the period from 1846 to 1852 the potato crops failed again and again. Famine hit hard. During the six blight years a million died of hunger and another million emigrated. Ireland's population started on a downward trend from eight to four million, near which it has tended to stabilize. Agriculture is more diversified now, but marriages are delayed in Ireland and over-all birth rates are low.

In the tropics, where extreme diversity is natural, simplification brings serious problems. Still, much of the commercial agriculture is monocultural in nature and often the economy of an entire region or nation is tied to the welfare of a single crop. Brazil's dependence on coffee and Cuba's on sugar are obvious examples. There are no real "banana republics" in Latin America today, but bananas have formed an extensive monoculture in many tropical American countries. Banana culture centered naturally on the broad lowland plains of the Caribbean and Gulf sides of Central America. Here it flourished in plantations that were mostly owned and controlled by foreign investors.

In the tropics agriculture often involves simplification of enormously complex ecosystems. Here the original rain forest is contrasted with a banana-coffee plantation. Such simplification sets in motion biological forces that would be held in check in the original diversified forest.

In the 1930s the banana monoculture was hit, as all mono-cultures must be, by a serious enemy. This was the Panama or sigatoka disease caused by a fungus parasite (*Cercospora musae*) which spread rapidly from plant to plant over the widespread plantations. The vigor and production of the banana plants were seriously reduced. In Costa Rica this caused the abandonment of commercial banana production in its previous center, the Caribbean lowlands, and its replacement there, in part, by more diversified crops. A new center of banana culture was established in the Golfo Dulce region on the Pacific coast of the country in an area free from disease. It was not until 1964, twenty-six years after the original move, that banana culture on a commercial scale was resumed once more on the Caribbean coast.

In tropical Mexico the banana blight also caused trouble. The region of Papaloapan on the Gulf Coast had long been a center for bananas and it yielded enough to put Mexico in the lead in banana exports. From the mid-1920s, when a commercial variety of banana, the Gros Michel, was introduced, until the 1930s, banana culture expanded rapidly. In 1938, however, the sigatoka disease arrived and spread everywhere. In 1941, with the banana harvest reduced 50 per cent, Standard Fruit Company, the main commercial producer, abandoned operations. By 1950 most of the banana area had gone to sugarcane or diversified crops. Only a few small areas continued to grow disease-resistant varieties of bananas, but these were not suited to the export trade. Both Mexico and Costa Rica survived, because they had other crops or industries to fall back on. If, like Ireland, they had depended on a monoculture, the story would be more tragic.

On the island of Mauritius a sugar monoculture has permitted populations to grow to a point where the island can be used as a demographic warning to the rest of the world. In 1720 there were no people on Mauritius, in 1800 there were 60,000; by 1851, 183,000. In the next thirty years the population doubled. Growth then leveled off for a time until the benefits of modern medicine reached Mauritius after World War II. By 1961 the population had reached 656,000 and was increasing at 3 per cent per year. These figures would not be large if it were not that Mauritius has only 720 square miles of land. The density is therefore around 900 to the square mile on an island with no resources except agricultural soils and some fish.

To quote Burton Benedict, who has studied the island: "The economy of Mauritius can be summed up in a single word, sugar . . . Over 40 per cent of the total land area of Mauritius is planted in sugar cane and this represents about 90 per cent of the arable land." The sugar industry, directly or indirectly, accounts for 70 per cent of the employment and 99 per cent of the value of the exports. All manufactured goods and most foods are imported.

Mauritius lies in the trade wind belt of the Indian Ocean east of Madagascar. Its balmy climate through much of the year is occasionally upset by devastating hurricanes, but in general it could be an ideal place for people. From the time of Vasco da Gama in the fifteenth century it provided a stopping-off place for ships bound around the Cape for Asia, and an equally attractive haven for pirates. In the seventeenth and eighteenth centuries the Dutch colonized it, but their efforts were not successful. They stayed long enough to exterminate the giant flightless pigeon, the dodo, which now stands as an example of how dead a thing can be. They also liberated domestic and other exotic animals and started the destruction of the native vegetation. The Dutch were followed by the French and in 1810 by the British. Mauritius became under the French a slave and sugar colony. Slavery was abolished by the British, but the former slaves remained and sugar continued as the dominant monoculture.

Mauritians have been subsidized to keep them alive, in the sense that Britain has guaranteed purchase of their sugar and insurance companies provide indemnity against loss of the crop. However, hurricanes have had devastating effects; 1892, 1931, 1945, 1960 and 1962 were bad hurricane years. The 1960 hurricanes cut exports to 62 per cent of their 1959 value and destroyed half of the homes on the island.

Obviously, dependence on a monoculture is precarious. If it fails, biologically or economically, there is nothing to fall back on. According to one report: "Hundreds of people are crowded

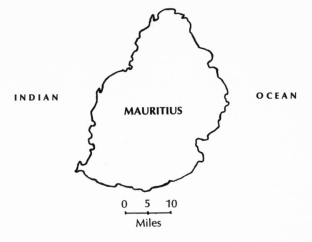

INDIAN   OCEAN

MAURITIUS

0   5   10

Miles

into tin shacks hardly fit for animals. Not surprisingly, tuber-
culosis and other diseases are very common in these slums, and
a large proportion of the families depend on the help, regular
and irregular, of the Public Assistance Department."

With diversified agriculture Mauritius could be an island
paradise for a small but happy population. It is on its way, with
monoculture, to becoming an island slum, keeping alive a large,
miserable population.

Unfortunately, what man does to protect his monocultures
often creates more havoc than the disease he set out to cure.
Some of our chemical companies have produced pesticides too
dangerous for use in the United States. The underdeveloped
world of the tropics, seeking any means to feed a few more
mouths, provides a lively market. A pesticide in the tropics becomes a doubly dangerous thing, for in this world controls have
been biological and not climatic.

G. R. Conway has described what has happened in Malaya
on the oil palm estates. A residual contact insecticide, of the
type described in *Silent Spring*, was used as a general prophy-
lactic with the view to controlling minor pests. Each time it
was used, however, it touched off an epidemic of bagworms,
which do serious damage to the palms. The bagworms were
then sprayed with more insecticide, which in turn produced a

still more severe outbreak. Finally, the spraying was abandoned and a selective insecticide, which kills only when eaten by the offending insect, was employed. Normal biological controls reasserted themselves, organisms harmful to bagworms appeared, and the infestations of bagworms declined to a tolerable level.

If this example is at all typical it is obvious that the chemical companies are on to a good thing. Their pesticides can create their own markets in the tropics, building plagues where none occurred before.

The eastern forests lost the chestnut to blight but are still rich, varied, and beautiful. What if there had been only chestnuts, cultivated for the benefit of man?

It would be misleading to leave the impression that diversity itself guarantees biological control of pests, or that diversified communities are by nature immune to epidemics or plagues. The eastern hardwood forests of the United States are as diversified as any forest community in the temperate zone. Nevertheless, an introduced disease, the chestnut blight, virtually eliminated the chestnut from the forests in which it grew. The savannah of Africa supports the most diversified group of wild mammals in the world. Still, rinderpest, introduced with cattle to Somaliland in the 1880s, swept from there to South Africa and decimated buffalo, eland, kudu, bushbuck, wildebeest and wild pigs. Yet these exceptions themselves provide a further argument for natural diversity. The eastern forests lost the chestnuts but they are still rich, varied and beautiful. What if there had been only chestnuts, cultivated for the benefit of man? The African fauna remained abundant and diversified despite rinderpest, and its populations once more recovered. How different it would have been if there were only a few species of value to man.

We could not afford to abandon our monocultural ways even if we wanted to. Yet the value of diversified agriculture and wild land is obvious. Diversified systems have built-in insurance against failures; simplified systems need constant care.

In earlier times we had much greater agricultural variety than we have today since in those days each farm family sought some degree of independence from uncertain and distant market-places. Carl Sauer has described the passing of the family farm in the Middle West: "The farm orchard, once as ubiquitous as the horse, is now about as rare. The common element was the apple tree of which there were numerous kinds, early and late ripening, preferred for eating out of hand, for baking, cider, apple butter. Some were favored varieties brought from the East with the original settlers. Others were of local origin, Missouri providing several kinds that became widely grown. A well kept orchard had a dozen kinds or more. . . . This spring I stopped on occasion to find an ancient apple or pear tree surviving in a flourishing stand of red cedar, or some forgotten planted plum in a thicket of briars. Once I saw hemmed in by cedars an Indian peach, a small frost resistant form that in manner unknown was handed on from Spaniards to southern Indian and to pioneer American settlers, and which reproduced 'true from the pits.'"

Now the farmers buy their apples in the supermarket from which all apples taste alike. One need not bite them to know their texture whatever name they may bear. We sacrificed our diversity for production quantity. We are richer but impoverished. Our money can't buy what we have lost. My children do not really know what an apple once tasted like, thus one could say they do not miss the flavor. But I grew up while there were still old orchards to be raided.

We cannot diversify the wheat fields of the Dakotas but we can plan for diversity where it will fit in. Even in the Dakotas there is room for difference on stream bank and roadside, around the potholes and the rough ground, around the farmhouses. We can't guarantee that it will give security to the wheat plants, but it will rest the eyes and enrich that quality known as landscape beauty.

It is a long jump from rain forests or wheat fields to cities, but the principles of diversity seem to hold equally well. Our suburbs are the equivalent of a monoculture, a single-species, even-aged stand of uniform housing. They lack natural viability because they lack the variety that would keep them alive and interesting. A little economic blight can sweep through them, decimating their populations, causing the houses to grow gray from lack of paint, to sag and decay. An industrial shutdown could start the process in many an area.

By contrast some of our diversified city neighborhoods seem to go on decade after decade resisting depression and prosperity alike, because they have the variety that attracts people from many parts of the world, many social levels and many occupations. Unfortunately the trend is and has been away from diversity. Our mass production methods are inimical to differences since it is easier and cheaper to build a standard high-rise or single-family dwelling with all parts precut or prefabricated. Thus we tend toward a monotony that leaves little room for individual choice, makes no allowance for the variety that still exists in mankind.

3

Tame People in Wild Lands

Man is not a machine that one can reconstruct as occasion demands, upon other lines for quite other ends, in the hope that it will then proceed to function, in a totally different way, just as normally as before. Man bears his age-long history with him; in his very structure is written the history of mankind.

—Carl G. Jung

I DON'T believe that our relatives, the chimpanzee and gorilla, give much thought to anything, but I am sure that they do not worry about nature. They have always been a part of it, ready to retreat from any close contact with their less hairy, human cousins, vanishing where man's activities destroy the forests on which they depend for food and shelter. But wild country is for them only habitat, the place where they find the necessities for living. Jane Goodall's remarkable studies in Africa have shown that chimpanzees have no fondness for wild forests as such. Once they learn not to fear they are willing to accept the easy living and ready food supply of civilization's camps. This knowledge probably would have worried Ernest Thompson Seton, who balanced his ability as a keen observer and a first-rate naturalist with a Victorian concern for the morals and manners of wild creatures, and even went so far as to write an animal's Ten Commandments. It worries me also, even though the morals of wild beasts do not. I foresee the destiny of wild animals that forsake the wild is the stew pot or the zoo.

The absence of any decent aesthetic sense among wild animals could also be disturbing if one allowed himself to brood about it. Nevertheless any national park visitor can observe the preference of bears for garbage cans. Birds show an easygoing attitude toward telephone poles, equating them with trees. Indeed if we succeed in putting all electric and telephone lines underground, we will decimate the populations of kingbirds, swallows, shrikes, sparrow hawks and woodpeckers that have used these man-made structures to extend their habitat. Wood rats and deer mice willingly make their homes in rural slums and ghost towns. The "dainty" deer and "lordly" elk pilfer crops from the most wretchedly ugly farmyards. If we are seeking a love of wild country and natural beauty, we had best confine our search to the human species.

Back before man was much advanced toward the human condition there was nothing in the world but wild country. Man was a wilderness species by necessity and not by choice until the time came when he developed the skills and tools needed to

Primitive man was a wilderness species by necessity. His first home may have been in the riverine forests of tropical Africa, where game would be abundant and the vegetation diverse. In the same region, in the wet season, the varied habitat around the rocky kopjes could provide food and shelter.

modify the landscape. Over tens of thousands of years, however, man evolved his social behavior and cultural attributes in wilderness environments, shaped by forces of fire and storm, abundance and scarcity, floods and droughts, predators and prey. The roots of our attitudes, drives, or perhaps they can be called instincts, that govern our activities today lie far back in our wilderness past, inherited perhaps from prehuman ancestors. There seems little doubt that man was one of the more aggressive of the various primates that competed for a dominant position on the face of the earth. I have heard Carl Sauer say that man was distinguished from other primates by his exceeding and constant bad temper. There is also little doubt that man's aggressive instincts were associated with his mammalian tendency to maintain and defend a territory, a home ground used only by himself or his group. These characteristics of man have long been known. Less emphasized, however, is the reverse side of this behavior. Man may have been a killer, but he is also the only animal that weeps over the slain. If aggression and territoriality are basic human traits, then sympathy and empathy are also human. Man destroys a forest but then feels ill at ease and builds a shrine to the spirits of the wood.

Man's relation to his environment and his retreat from the wilderness began with the first great human revolution, that brought by the domestication of animals and plants. With agriculture and the husbandry of livestock there was for the first time a new kind of landscape on earth, one man-made, built from tamed things. The food patch, then the garden and finally the plowed field appeared and began to occupy an ever-increasing area of land. The agricultural village replaced the hunter's or food gatherer's camp and began to provide some degree of isolation from the complete wildness of surrounding nature. Permanent trails spread out, and were to widen into roads that connected the tamed areas in which man had an interest. From village centers, tamed flocks and herds moved out to start a pattern of change on the wilder lands.

Perhaps everywhere man's first land-management tool, fire, went with him or before him to open up woodland and scrub, create fresh clearings for grazing or farming, build up the

The savannah landscape of woodland and grass may have been largely created and maintained by man's use of fire.

savannah landscape of alternating woodland and glade that seems even today to symbolize man's habitat. This savannah is worth some contemplation. The diversity within it seems essential to man's feeling of well-being. Anyone who has flown over eastern United States has seen the alternating pattern of woodland and glade that man has formed in place of the older, more continuous forest. In the prairies and the plains each farmhouse has its trees where once there was only grass.

Perhaps the woodland grove originally represented shelter from the elements and security from the lions and wild dogs that ranged the grasslands. But it would only feel secure if it were small in extent since otherwise it would be too accessible to those other enemies that range the forested lands. The grassland or open space as the predominant element of the landscape would give, to a creature who depended mostly on eyesight to warn him of danger, the feeling that he could see anything that approached his wooded hiding place. Even today we find few peoples adapted to entirely open or entirely forested areas. For most humans the contrasts seem important; when they settle in the grasslands they plant trees, when they settle in the forest

Agriculture brought a new kind of landscape, not before found on earth, adding at first to natural diversity.

they make clearings. The phenomenon of edge, or interspersion, well known to wildlife biologists, may have entered into man's original choice of habitat. Edges are areas that support the greatest variety of game, and also the greatest variety of accessible, easily reached food plants. Today the wildlife that is attracted by interspersion adds to the interest of the woodland and glade environment.

The greatest separation of man from the wild country that was his early home came when the rich soils of the river basins produced the food surpluses that would support dense, permanent populations. With the subsequent rise of cities and civilization a largely artificial world could be created. Behind the city wall more natural things could be, for a while, forgotten. People could glory in the works of man and lose contact with ways and things that were wild. The old earth spirits could be forgotten in the worship of new deities of power and violence.

There is little evidence that those who shared the greater comfort and security of the early cities felt any great nostalgia for the wild lands that had supported their ancestors. Yet they did bring a share of nature with them when they could, and the Biblical paradise was not a city but a garden. It is true also that those who had a greater share of material things, the aristocracy of earlier times, used their leisure in hunting expeditions to the

With higher culture and civilization man's retreat from nature began.

Behind city walls more natural things could be, for a while, forgotten.

wild country, sought "wild-land recreation" as a change from the city routine. Yet most brought the trappings of civilization with them on their hunts, and showed little inclination to rough it, or no more than the present-day tourist with his luxury trailer, camping in the "wilderness." The account of a hunt engaged in by Kubla Khan, whose immediate ancestors roamed the wild plains of Asia, is illustrative:

"The Emperor himself is carried upon four elephants in a fine chamber made of timber, lined inside with plates of beaten gold, and outside with lion's skins (for he always travels in this way on his fowling expeditions, because he is troubled with gout). He always keeps beside him a dozen of his choicest ger-falcons, and is attended by several of his Barons, who ride on horseback alongside." When he finally reaches his hunting camp he finds: "The tent in which he holds his courts is large enough to give cover easily to a thousand souls. . . . Immediately behind the great tent there is a fine large chamber where the Lord sleeps. . . . Each of the audience tents has three poles, which are of spice-wood, and are most artfully covered with lion's skins striped with black and white and red, so that they do not suffer from any weather." Perhaps it is not fair to say that the Great Khan was seeking a "wilderness experience," or perhaps, for his rank and position, this was the closest thing to wilderness that he could manage.

During all of the thousands of years when man was moving from a wilderness existence to one dependent on agriculture and then upon civilization, he was creating not less, but more diversity. The agricultural fields added variety to the wild hills. The lands of Mesopotamia, during the flowering of the early civilizations, were enriched and not impoverished by the presence of cities, villages, fields and gardens. It was only when the herds grew too numerous, when the fields spread too far, when too many woodlands were cut down that variety was endangered, that the uniformity of a man-made landscape began to dominate.

Sometimes I like to speculate on what the world would be like if things had happened differently. Suppose, for example, human population increase had stabilized at the levels reached during the times of Alexander the Great. If thereafter births and deaths had been in some rough balance. There is no reason to believe that technology would not still have advanced. Perhaps the industrial revolution and its electronic aftermath might still have occurred. Greek science was well advanced, Roman technology is not to be sneered at even today; the Chinese were in many ways even farther down the technological road. But with only a few hundred million people on earth and the whole wide world for their work and play, man might have managed the benefits of high culture while still maintaining all the mystery and variety of wild nature. Such imaginings as these can help illuminate the concept of population optima. We have probably long since passed a population level under which we could have really enjoyed the world that we inherited.

It is easy to fall into the trap of thinking that with the rise of civilization most people moved into cities or had close association with cities, and that was the end of man's close relationship with nature. Such an impression arises because city people left the records, did most of the writing, and were concerned with the things that seemed important to them. Most of humanity, however, remained until very recent times quite apart from city living. They carried on in their old diverse ways, farming and fishing, hunting and herding, while cities rose and fell without their knowledge. They lived in environments as diverse as their own cultures, grew attached to their own landscapes, their hills or their deserts, felt lost and forlorn when circumstances removed them from their homelands. Their hearts were in the Highlands, or by Galway Bay; they felt they were "forever England," or they yearned for the banks of the Zambesi. They felt that they were "the people," the Bantu, or that "only a Mongol has true heart," and they belonged to their land.

From the dawn of civilization down through thousands of years until the latter part of the nineteenth century, wilderness dominated the face of the earth and lands that were much affected by man were small in extent. Even for those who lived apart from the wilderness in the farmlands or cities, the presence of wilderness was a constant factor; its existence an influence on the human spirit. At worst it was the unknown haunt of beast and barbarian beyond the known frontier. At best it could be that place "between the desert and the sown, where name of slave and sultan is forgot." Always there was the knowledge that the world was large, full of wonders, often frightening, sometimes awe inspiring. Always there were some who believed that beyond the far horizons were uncharted lands where anything could happen and any miracle become a reality. Men could dream and spin the stories that became fairy tales, but then seemed almost true. Following dreams, explorers could go out into the wilderness and return with tales of the unbelievable. Braving the wilds, colonists went out to fight the hazards and dangers and extend the domain of man.

Down the centuries the wild country was there to test man's mettle.

On down the centuries the wild country was there to test man's mettle, to provide him with hope for a different world if he had but the courage to find it or create it. It was the land over the mountains or beyond the sea; it was as real to some as the air that they breathed. Nobody questioned it, nobody attempted to define it. But then, suddenly, it was gone. People began to wonder what it had meant and how to describe it. They were to argue whether the bits and pieces of still untouched land that remained really qualified as wilderness at all. Faced with a world in which there was no "country beyond," trapped by a technological civilization that few could understand, they were to spin a new set of fairy tales that could be true, of flying saucers and little men from Mars, seeking to create beyond the horizons of outer space a new dream of wondrous lands where miracles could happen, and some new El Dorado or Shangri-La, some Avalon or Saint Brendan's Isle, might yet be found.

It is a rule of economics and of life that values follow scarcity and we do not miss things of value until we have lost them, or nearly so. The old saying was "you never miss the water 'til the well goes dry." Wilderness as such was not much appreciated until civilization was too widespread and the opportunity to escape from its surfeit of blessings and conflicts seemed important. Wilderness values belong to a civilization that provides an abundance of the necessities of life. Primitive people show a remarkable willingness to forsake the wild lands for the city, even where this means living in the most wretched slum. Security counts more for them than aesthetics, more than liberty. Even in America, appreciation for wilderness is often most pronounced in city folk.

Whether or not wilderness in the old sense of the word has disappeared, wild lands remain and in one form or another always will. There are mountains too rough for our settlement, deserts too stony or sterile for irrigation, tundras too wet or frozen for permanent use. Wild lands have always formed a part of the human environment. The old wilderness might attract the rebel, the wanderer or the immigrant band, but wild lands were part of home. They were available to any who might tire of the pressures of camp, village or city, and want to get away for a while. They were used by the wood gatherer, the timber cutter, the herdsmen or the hunters who sought their products for material gain, and by others who wanted only to enjoy the solitude or open space. There was some conflict between these two groups even in the days before Christ, and those who complained of the timber cutters and the goats and wished for the good old days before man had defaced the landscape. But these conflicts were few when wild land was plentiful and always surrounded the tame. Today, when the available wild space has diminished, these conflicts become a major concern.

Wild land, whether in the form of open space around the city or some distant wilderness, has grown in importance as its availability has diminished. But importance it has always had. It has been valued as a safety valve against the pressures of crowding and of too great demand for conformity to the group. F. Fraser Darling, writing of the Western Highlands of Scotland, has described this role:

"To return to the Highlands: the destruction of the forests has meant the removal of cover, and this environmental factor is of great importance in human lives. Humanity needs cover for all sorts of things—shelter for crops and stock; cover to enable a man to do a little experimentation which he dare not try if the eyes of every household in the township are upon him; and cover for courting and love-making. It is obvious what a social problem lack of cover imposes in certain types of urban communities. In the Highlands it has imposed a set of conventions almost the exact opposite of our own. Darkness is the only cover, but this is supplemented by a build-up of psychological cover. The Tiree crofter visits the Duke of Argyll's factor on the nights of no moon, though he could just as well go in the day. A fellow and a girl in the Hebrides will ignore each other in daytime should they meet on the road, but he will be calling at her home just about the time of night when in our culture we should have taken our leave. Good manners require that he be gone before it is light.

"I have mentioned the value of cover in experimentation. We tend to forget how important it is in primitive communities that people should not be different, and the initial attempts to be different are the most dangerous ones. Think how in our own lives we like to experiment in private and avoid being different in the beginning. The Anglo-Saxon races have a firm belief in the power of demonstration in changing methods of doing things. This is a fallacy. The Gael or the Mexican is wiser. It does not matter that a changed practice will reap him a bigger material reward. That is not recompense for having to that extent placed himself outside his group. If the material reward is real, he will be envied by his fellows, and that is not a good state to be in. If the reward is illusory, he will be ridiculed, and that is not good either in a society where there is no privacy."

Darling's description of the role of cover can apply also to wild lands in general. To a degree the modern metropolis has taken over some of the old role of wild country in providing escape and privacy. Its size and vast number of transient people provide an anonymity that does not exist in a smaller community. However, the city fails in other respects and the pressure of great numbers alone brings a need for escape. We hear much today of the break-up of the former extended family group, of the lack of feeling of neighborhood and community in urban areas. These are legitimate worries. Yet we will always need also an escape from too much "togetherness." Failure to provide this may well aggravate man's innate feelings of aggressive territoriality, a dangerous prospect in today's tense world.

There is an importance of wild land to the maintenance of freedom from social restraint. One notes the increased restrictions on individual behavior that are imposed where populations grow dense. Particularly in our highly technological societies, such restrictions are essential to avoid chaos, and the more rigid they become the greater is the need to avoid them. Jacquetta Hawkes, in describing the pressures of population, has said of people in crowded cities that "They are in danger like passengers in an overloaded boat, and must be shepherded, planned for, and always of necessity handled in vast groups with their impersonal, clumsy relationships." Many people who would "like to fight for a reasonable anarchism are fearful to venture for

fear it might lead to stampede or breakdown among the enormous urban populations where no one is able to keep himself
alive if trade or services fail."

To one born in the twentieth century in an industrial society
the lack of freedom to go where you please when you please is
taken for granted and further rules and restrictions upon behavior are hardly noted. A Rip van Winkle, however, awakening
after the sleep of a century, might believe that liberty had vanished from his homeland. At the very start he would be stopped
by his inability to establish his personal identity. Without docu-
ments, records of birth, education and employment, he would
become a non-person in our society. In a freer age it would be
enough to remember your own name and have an honest face.

The loss of freedom in our society is not a simple matter,
since in some ways we have greater freedom than ever before,
freedom in the sense of opportunity in education and employment, in the sense that we can afford a high degree of personal
mobility, in the sense that we live in a basically friendly and
benevolent society rather than one hostile and cruel. Yet old
restrictions on our activities by nature have been replaced by
new ones imposed by man and these seem more irksome. Not
long ago a man could travel anywhere in the world without
restriction, impeded only by his financial resources and his
ability to move himself on foot, horseback, horse-drawn coach
or sailing vessel. Now we can theoretically go anywhere on
earth, within a day, but we are restricted by the barriers that
nations have erected to keep foreigners and their products under
control. Admittedly this is a small restriction compared to the
older ones, but it irritates because it often seems unnecessary.
The need to carry one's identity cards and records with him
is obviously compensated by the personal and economic security
that these provide. In an earlier day one carried no papers, but
the stranger was often roughly treated. It is a matter of degree.
One fears a trend toward increasing restriction, toward the day
when nobody can ever go anywhere new for a fresh start, toward
the day when a computerized dossier follows one forever. Wild
land offers a buffer. At least there, for a time, one can escape
his social identity and be only a human alone with nature and

Wild land offers a buffer . . . one can be only a human alone with nature and his own memories. (*Photograph courtesy of National Park Service*)

his own memories, watched over by a God who does not interfere.

I would like to argue for a relationship between political freedom and wild country, but the ground is difficult. America has political freedom and an abundance of wild land. Russia, however, has even more open space and yet rigid control over the social, economic and political life of all individuals. The over-crowded lowlands of China are backed by wild highlands, yet freedom has not flourished. Political freedom and lack of open space go together in the Low Countries of Europe and to a lesser extent in Great Britain. One could argue a relationship between the resistant Highlands of the Scots, the rough Welsh mountains, the moors and forests of England, and the evolution of British freedom. One could argue for the role of the open spaces of the Empire in the maintenance of that freedom, and question whether it will persist now that the Empire has gone and Britons are forced to look inward and contemplate each other. But at-tractive though this argument may be, it is difficult to maintain. There is no clear correlation between open space and political freedom. There remains, however, a relationship between wild country and the opportunity for escape from tyranny.

Throughout the world wild country has provided a refuge for the political opposition in lands where tyranny flourished as well as in lands where an outcast minority sought to take the reins of power. The examples are many. The partisans in the forests of Russia and the mountains of Yugoslavia hastened the downfall of German power in the Second World War. The brush-covered mountains of France gave the name of their vegetation to the French resistance, the Maquis. The forests and mountains of Cuba sheltered Castro against Batista's troops, and shelter Castro's opposition today. In Korea and now in Vietnam the key to victory may rest in the hands of those who learn to use the wild country to their advantage. Wild land is then a shelter for the rebel. Dictators must fear wild mountains. Free men, who wish to remain free, had best learn the ways of wild country.

Finally, we have in wild country and open space values that are to some the most important—the opportunity they provide for reestablishment of contact with nature. Man has a degree of wildness in his soul, and needs occasionally to establish contact with things that are not man-made, that grow and live without his guidance, that make no demands upon him. When a fellow human speaks we feel we must listen and try to comprehend. When a bird sings it asks for no such commitment. We feel appreciation or not as we please. A natural landscape does not need our participation. It is there for no purpose of ours, or it can offer whatever we care to see, feel or learn about it. Man has been too long in nature to be cut off from it entirely without spiritual or psychological ill effects. We all seek some elements of our old wildness, even if only a pet dog, a garden, a city park or a view from the road.

This is all part of the question of diversity, variety and opportunity for change. Lewis Mumford has said it well:

"When we rally to preserve the remaining redwood forests or to protect the whooping crane, we are rallying to preserve ourselves, we are trying to keep in existence the organic variety, the

When we rally to preserve wildness we are rallying to preserve ourselves.

whole span of natural resources upon which our own further development will be based. If we surrender this variety too easily in one place, we shall lose it everywhere; and we shall find ourselves enclosed in a technological prison, without even the hope that sustains a prisoner in jail—that someday we may get out. Should organic variety disappear, there will be no 'out.'"

It is easy enough to sell Americans on the value of the pieces of wilderness we have left. It is difficult to go to other countries and convince the custodians of the earth's really wild lands of their importance. I recall once on the long road between Bula-wayo and Victoria Falls trying to convey to an African friend of mine some picture of what Europe and America were like. After explaining that I was of German and Irish background and that the Irish and Germans were sort of tribes, like the Matabele and the Mashona, and that London was a bigger city than Salisbury, I gave up and started brooding. None of these Africans I knew, who would have to build a new nation to take

Nobody who has not felt the cold impersonality of a technological civilization can fully appreciate a waterhole where game come to drink and at which a lion may roar.

its place in the modern world, had any real conception of that world. The planes came and the planes went at the airport, carrying people back and forth to it, but they might just as well be spaceships from another planet. These Africans had all around them a world that we had forever lost, and they were prepared to give it up for a place at the technological dinner table. Nobody who has not felt the cold impersonality of a technological society can really appreciate a herd of giraffes coming in to drink at a water hole in a twilight in which a lion roars. Nobody who has not contemplated Hiroshima can realize that among the ways available in which a man can die, it is a rare and signal distinction to be killed by a leopard.

In just a few decades we have moved a long way in America from our own wild past. In the settlement of this country the desire for freedom and the availability of wild land interacted. The colonists who came to the New World were not hardy seekers for the glories of wild nature. Mostly they came from the cities and settled farmscapes of Europe, driven to escape persecution for their religious beliefs, driven by a desire to escape the hopelessness of lower class or peasant life, or simply shipped out because they had run afoul of some capricious law. Many had no ability to cope with the harsh American environment, and were overwhelmed by it, dying of hunger or exposure. Others waged a desperate fight to beat back the wilderness, establish the farms that could feed and the villages that could shelter them from hostile weather and hostile natives. Few appreciated the glories of the wild land that surrounded them. Many complained of its desolation and savagery. Most were content to stay close to the settled lands on the continental shore.

The availability of new lands, however, held always an open door of greater freedom and opportunity for those who wished to take it. There was no need to stay bound to the family farm, or to accept the peck order of the home village. Those with self-reliance and courage were free to exercise these qualities. The wilderness offered a livelihood for those who cared to hunt, fish or trap. It offered timber for new homes, grass for livestock, new soil to grow new crops. Initially its immense size relative to the number of people available to settle it colored all attitudes toward it.

The settlers of America came mostly from lands where a peasant or yeoman tradition had long been established. With such tradition there is a feeling of attachment to and responsibility for the land. Land is security, food, clothing, for oneself, one's family, one's heirs. Care of the land guarantees prosperity. The peasant seeks to sink roots, establish a home where the young will be born, near hallowed ground where the old will be buried. Even the modern peasant is not far from a past when the earth goddess was worshiped and the spirits of the ancestors were seldom far away. Such a tradition came to America with some groups of farmers. It has produced those cared-for and cherished farmlands in Pennsylvania and Ohio and on to Iowa. But it was not a dominant tradition. Most settlers were not peasants and were poor farmers.

An attitude that was to characterize much of the exploration and early settlement of America was that of transient exploitation by people who felt no allegiance to place. The fur trapper who led the way into the North and West usually did not plan to

Soils washed into rivers.

remain in the wild country or to care for the lands and the animals that enriched him. The hide hunter who pursued the buffalo had no interest in taking only an annual crop from the wild herds. The nomadic stockman who ground the western plains to dust was a transient on the land who could not care less if tomorrow it blew away. The logger who hacked and burned his way through the northern forests did not worry about the ghost towns and fire-scarred lands that were left behind. Those who planted corn, tobacco and cotton where once were forests in the South knew that when the soils were exhausted there was new land out West. All sought wealth through exploitation of wild-land resources, wealth that would buy them status and position in some more urbane place. Where they passed through, wildlife vanished and forests were no more; soils washed into rivers or blew in the dust clouds of summer, rangelands became deserts.

As the frontier vanished and populations grew, as cities spread and the extent of our resources finally became evident, the role of the plunderer was restricted. With no new land, men must stay where land was available and assume some responsibility for it. As public control was exercised over both public and private lands, the opportunities for exploitation were further restricted. Yet there were those who could not manage to change; who lacked the knowledge or the capital to exercise good management; whose lives were eroded along with the soils that had

Rangelands became deserts.

Antelope once more returned to the plains. (*Photograph by James D. Yoakum*)

supported them; and who finally fled under the dust clouds of the thirties, leaving battered landscapes behind. Even today, transient exploitation by those who feel that their home and allegiance is elsewhere is a factor in the land. It leads to raw mining towns in the western desert, to carelessly flung-up real estate tracts, to the strip mines and barren lives in the "pockets of poverty" in Appalachia, to the gouging of those western forests where the contract logger still finds room to operate.

But the lands and life of America are for the most part tough and resistant. Forests and grasslands and the soils that support them have survived drought and fire, flood and blizzard, heat and bitter cold, the trampling of wild hooves, long before man appeared on the scene. The vegetation comes back following the sometimes slow processes of plant succession. Weeds invade and put a cover of green over bare soil. Perennial herbs grow in to replace the annuals. Prairie grasses or forest trees follow and regain the ground once lost. As the land recovers, the animals that lived there, if not exterminated, gradually return. Grouse fly once more in the hardwood forests and antelope return to the plain. The raw soils of abandoned cotton fields are invaded by yellow pines and then by the wild turkey. Grama and buffalo grasses extend their rhizomes to cover the bare places left by the hooves of too many sheep. If the exploiter does not come back the ravages can be repaired. Over much of America the exploiter was not allowed to return. Other forces were operating in America that acted to stabilize, protect and conserve. Sometimes these forces were backed by those who were once among the transients and the plunderers.

Few people are devoid of a social conscience, although among some it is severely repressed. Even fewer are devoid of a desire for personal gain—wealth, power or prestige. The two interests are often in conflict. Sometimes the one operates for a time at the expense of the other, but when its demands are met the other takes over. A man who has accrued a fortune at the expense of the land may use the fortune to repair and restore and end up by doing more good than damage.

In America the social conscience, expressed as concern for the American environment, became active early in our history and gained increasing strength as the damage done by exploitation became obvious to all. It led to the establishment of forest reserves and national parks, to government activity in soil conservation and land management, and finally to a concern for the quality of our cities and for natural beauty everywhere. Through its gathering strength it was able to slow down, inhibit and sometimes prevent entirely those activities that lead to destruction of lands and natural resources.

Today as we approach the end of the fifth century that has passed since Columbus sighted America, we are caught up in a land with no frontiers and only sample patches of the old wilderness. Hurricanes of social and technological change sweep over our lands and all the world. We seek desperately to maintain old qualities of living, to preserve those landmarks that tell us of our past, while we gaze into an uncertain future. In our century we seek as never before to retain and restore beauty and wildness in our lands, yet we have set in motion more powerful forces of destruction than we seem capable of controlling. For the first time in our history the innate ability of our people to increase and multiply forms a threat against our continued existence as free men in a free land.

4

To Save or to Destroy

And every place he came to settle
He spread with gadgets saving toil,
He even had a whistling kettle
To warn him it was on the boil.
Beneath the waratahs and wattles
Baronia and coolibah,
He scattered paper, cans and bottles,
And parked his nasty little car.
                                    —John Manifold

IN THE spring of the year there is a stirring of activity over all America. In millions of garages and backyard sheds boats are receiving their final coat of paint, fishing gear is being unlimbered, boots are being oiled and ten million sleeping bags are put out in the sun for airing. When the warmth of June brings out the roses there is a roar of motors across the land, and where the bison once roamed the migratory hordes of tourists now surge across the plains. Into all the mountains, up all the streams, across the lakes they move. Out from their stinking cities they come to stake their claim to the wild lands of America. To them the boundaries between the private lands and public seem indistinct. If the land looks wild they have a claim to it. The future of all the land is what they decide that it will be.

During the year 1965 I had the dubious honor of being chairman of the natural resources division of Humboldt State College, located 285 highway miles, or six tourist hours, north of San Francisco. Arcata lies in the heart of the redwood region and modestly advertises itself as "the lumber center of the world." In northwestern California 1965 can be remembered as the second and most heated year of the Redwood National Park controversy. Humboldt State College proved to be one of the battlegrounds of the redwood war. The conflict served to illustrate the differences between urban and rural interests in wild country. Regardless of how it is resolved it will leave deep wounds and bitter feelings on both sides. It is part of the struggle to preserve diversity in this country, a struggle in which attention must first be given to the wild lands, since these are the background against which all other forms of diversity, man-made variety, must take shape.

It would be comforting to have all issues clear cut, to have good guys and bad guys, black and white, conserver for the public interest and exploiter for private greed. But life is not simple, and I envy those who see it that way. My own sympathies go with the Sierra Club, the National Park Service and others who seem clearly allied with the angels. When I heard Justice

People seeking outdoor recreation crowd the beaches and occupy the national parks. The future of all land is what they decide it will be. (*Photograph below courtesy of National Park Service*)

William O. Douglas give one of his stirring orations on the redwoods I could not disagree with the spirit he represented. But I started my career as a forester, and for brief periods wore the pine-tree badge and green jacket of the Forest Service. When lumber company foresters speak, or the representatives of the timber companies, the words I hear also strike a responsive chord. Furthermore in an age when government tends to dominate private action to an unprecedented degree, I have a sympathy for those who want to fight for more individual initia-

Redwoods dominate the valleys of California's north coastal rivers. (*Photograph courtesy of Swanlund Photo Laboratory*)

tive. I recall the owner of a small redwood company who spoke out indignantly at a meeting: "What hurts me most in all this national park talk is the way they say 'our redwoods.' What do they mean *our* redwoods. They're *mine*. I bought them and I pay taxes on them." Considering the temper of these times, his was a voice from an earlier age. But I could not help wishing that the world in which he thought he was living still existed somewhere. There was space in it, after all, and even room enough for such a thing as *private* land. But his world has gone. We have become crowded voyagers on a small planet and the public interest must prevail.

The redwoods represent wild country, stretching north and south from a metropolitan region in which nearly four million people have crowded in a state with the fastest rate of population growth in America. They occur in a coastal strip from central California north, barely entering the southern fringe of Oregon. In the far south along the ocean shores of the Santa Lucias they occupy the more sheltered canyons where they are dwarfed in size and twisted in shape. Farther north they find a more suitable environment where the Big Sur streams make their way to the coast south of Carmel, and here some groves of fair-sized trees occur. There is a break north of Monterey, but redwoods dominate in the canyons of the Santa Cruz mountains. Extensive groves occurred here in the past, but most have been cut over. This is a tension zone between redwoods and the more drought-resistant oaks and chaparral, and the balance can easily be tipped in favor of the latter.

North of San Francisco Bay there are some scattered groves in Marin County, one of which, Muir Woods, is the only grove under national park jurisdiction at this time. Again there is a gap in Sonoma County until the vicinity of the Russian River is reached. From there northward the redwood forests dominate along the coast and the valleys of coastal rivers and reach without any sizable break to the Oregon border region. Forests in which redwoods occur as a dominant tree are estimated to have occupied nearly two million acres when the West was first settled. Most of that acreage has been cut-over, cleared off, burned or otherwise modified as a result of human use of the land. This does not mean that the redwoods have gone. Over most of this range they persist, but in young, second-growth stands in place of the primeval forests of ancient giants. There is no danger of losing "the last redwoods." There is danger of losing most of the remaining virgin forests.

The old redwood groves are hard to surpass in forest beauty, but it should be understood that they are not the oldest trees, since several species live to a riper age, and a redwood older than a thousand years is unusual. They may not even be the tallest trees, since one of America's douglas-firs has grown taller, and some of Australia's gums may have surpassed their height.

The old groves are hard to surpass in forest beauty.

Yet, let there be no mistake, they are tall, reaching up to nearly 370 feet, ancient and impressive. The oldest trees may have been alive when the Roman Empire died; the youngest may see the last of all of us. We owe it to all humanity to see that enough of the old groves are saved. In the heat of the redwood controversy it would have been well to remember that nobody was in any essential disagreement about saving old redwood groves. The fight was over the question of how much.

In 1964 it was estimated that there were no more than three hundred thousand acres of virgin redwood forest left in the world, and of this only fifty thousand acres had been preserved in California's state parks. Most of the rest was in lumber company ownership. The greater part of it was located in the far northwest of California, in Humboldt and Del Norte Counties. These acreage figures are reasonably accurate, since they can be obtained from aerial photographs. Figures that have been published on the actual volume of redwood timber remaining in these primeval forests need be viewed with more suspicion. Thus, one redwood park advocate stirred up a heated controversy, and rated a special editorial in a Humboldt County newspaper, denouncing him personally, by using published figures on timber volumes and rates of cutting to prove that the old-growth forests would be exhausted by 1968. The indignation of the timber owners was compounded by the realization that their own business policies constrained them from revealing the figures on volume and cut from which they presumably were deriving their statement of a twenty to forty year supply of old-growth redwood.

In 1964-65 it was obvious to all that the last extensive stands of virgin redwood forest were being cut down, sawed into logs, transported to mills and converted to redwood lumber and other commodities highly prized by consumers throughout the nation. There was nothing unusual about this process. Redwood logging, as a commercial enterprise, had been going on in northern California for more than a century. In the mid-twentieth century the lumber companies were better behaved than in earlier times. Most employed professional foresters. Most were interested in seeing that the forests grew back so that the redwood timber

Redwood logging has been going on for more than a century.

industries could stay in business. However, the cutting of a two
hundred to three hundred foot redwood tree is not the same as
the falling of a small pine or spruce. When a giant falls lesser
beings may be crushed. When a redwood log is hauled from the
woods, things that stand in the way get beaten and battered.
When a grove of redwoods is logged over the results cannot be
pleasing to the eye. Nor had any thought been given by the
loggers to the need for maintaining natural beauty on logged-
over lands. Indeed in the mid-1960s a form of clear-cutting with
maximum exposure of "mineral soil" was becoming accepted in
the redwood region. This left the country looking like the far
side of hell. City folk driving up to see the great forests were
shocked.

Concern for the preservation of redwood forests is almost as
old as the interest in converting them to lumber. It led through
the years to various drives for conservation by the timber owners
themselves, by various private philanthropists such as John D.

Rockefeller, by civic groups of many kinds of which the Save-the-Redwoods League is outstanding, and by the state of California. The result was the excellent state park system of California, with fifty thousand acres of virgin redwoods saved from cutting. In 1963, however, the dwindling supply of primeval forest, combined with the disgraceful appearance of the cut-over lands, caused a public demand for extension of protection over more of the remaining virgin redwood area. Some wanted to call a halt to all further logging of old-growth redwood. Others wanted varying degrees of extension of the protective park system. The rallying point for all who were interested in further protection of redwoods became the proposal advanced by the National Park Service in 1964, calling for a Redwood National Park to be located in northern Humboldt and Del Norte Counties. The publication of this proposal was also the signal for the timber industries to rally all of their supporters and prepare for a prolonged battle with the National Park Service.

When a giant falls lesser beings may be crushed. (*Photograph courtesy of Swanlund Photo Laboratory*)

Selective logging in pine country can leave a tidy landscape. In redwood country, loggers leave a battered area behind them.

Other public agencies in the redwood country moved quickly to neutral ground and pretended for a time that the struggle was no concern of theirs. But neutral ground was hard to hold, and in time the redwood region had two camps: those labeled "preservationists," who were for the park, and those labeled "industry people," who were against it. Not strangely, many who opposed the park and waved banners calling for "sustained-yield" timber harvesting, and "multiple-use" of forest resources, were the same people who some decades earlier had fought another battle to prevent the Forest Service from moving into the redwood region. In those days the concepts of sustained-yield and multiple-use, advocated by the Forest Service, were anathema to the advocates of uninhibited free enterprise in the redwood region. But those were the days of lumber barons and company towns, open seasons on union organizers and general public-be-damned attitudes that are embarrassing to recall today. I remember hearing the founder of the so-called Redwood Region Conservation Council, an industry-sponsored group with a somewhat restricted view of conservation, giving an impassioned speech about how they had won this earlier battle against the federal boys and the "bleeding-heart conservationists" of earlier times. But in the 1960s the local Forest Service representatives and the timber industries shared a common outlook. The board-foot bias of the nation's forestry schools had done its work.

With the development of a major national park controversy, truth vanished from the redwoods. It was no longer possible for a "preservationist" to obtain the correct time of day from an "industry man," let alone figures on timber acreage, rates of cutting, regrowth or other data of significance. Cries of lies, distortion, intimidation and misrepresentation were shouted through the redwood groves. To confuse the issue further the park advocates split into factions, each with a pet park plan and a willingness to suspect all others of selling out. In my position with the college I found difficulty in administering an organization whose members insisted on taking extreme positions on all sides of the battle. Between attempts to placate delegations from industry who clearly wanted the scalp of an extreme park advocate, faculty groups who were zealously guarding academic freedom and pro-park groups who wanted the college to denounce the industry, there seemed little time for anything else.

Behind the conflict lay vast areas of ignorance and confusion, glossed over by the arguing factions. Behind the conflict also were great areas of general agreement, ignored in the sheer joy of battle. The rules of warfare demanded that a park be either a "good thing" or a "bad thing." Questions on what kind of a park, for what purposes, were not given much attention.

Great ignorance was revealed on the subject of redwood ecology. Indeed, so many conflicting statements were made about the redwood forests, each one presumably based on ecological studies, that the science of ecology gained a tarnished image in the redwood region. In fact the ecology of the redwoods had been studied inadequately and some aspects had not been studied at all. Sound statistical descriptions of redwood forest communities were scarce, and for the region as a whole absent, although there was an abundance of data on the redwood trees themselves, viewed as board feet of timber.

Buried deep within the controversy and scarcely mentioned was a basic reason for the bitterness and downright hatred. This came to my attention some years earlier when, as a new assistant professor, I sat silently at lunch with a number of local industrial tycoons. As the conversation among them progressed I was made to see through their eyes that the then Republican administration of President Eisenhower was so far to the left as to be virtually in the Russian camp. All forms of government interference with the rights of property, particularly the right to make a profit from land and its products, were regarded as evidence of socialist subversion of the American way of life. The national park question therefore was not, in the eyes of many local business and industrial leaders, a simple question of federal purchase of their lands and timber at a price to be agreed upon, but a final, all-out socialist assault upon one of the last outposts of free-enterprise capitalism. Obviously such a struggle called for desperate means. These included threats against the future employment, profits and livelihood of some who thought that they were only advocating an acceptable American-style national park.

Northwestern California is a rural region in which the only city is a small town of less than thirty thousand, and in which most people earn their living from the land. Attitudes toward this land differ strongly from those of city people. City dwellers tend to regard open land as representing in some degree common land. They are inclined to hunt on it, picnic on it, hike through it and generally use it as they would a national forest. Land with buildings on it is regarded as private, but land that is simply being used for growing trees or grazing cattle is never quite considered to be private. Even fences and signs do not change this attitude much. Hence the city dweller runs into conflict with the rural land owner, who regards his land as totally his own, somewhat sacred, and who can see no public rights to it. In northwestern California the rural interests, and in particular, timber interests, controlled the government and the political authority. In the state as a whole the same interests had little influence. For most Californians the redwoods were "our redwoods" and the particular individuals who happened to be holding legal title to the land each had only one vote and no special rights.

A recurrent theme in the redwood conflict became the recreational value of a national park, measured in terms of the tourist income that would be attracted to the redwood region. Park advocates insisted that the great flow of tourists to the new redwood park would more than offset any loss in local income caused by removing timber from the tax rolls and lumberjacks from the payrolls. Park opponents scoffed at this idea and maintained the the economy of the region would be crippled by a national park. The newly created Bureau of Outdoor Recreation was drawn into the battle and asked to provide an answer to this question. It was not allowed funds for the research needed to devise ways to find such an answer.

The issue of tourism and recreation suggested to some that the primary purpose of the park was to attract vast numbers of people who would be provided with a "redwood recreational experience." To accomplish this, presumably, recreational facilities of all kinds were to be provided in the newly preserved redwood forests. The extent to which such facilities might con-

Old-growth redwood stands often contain dense undergrowth and fallen trees. Sword ferns may grow in jungle-like masses. (*Humboldt State College photograph by Charles F. Yocom*)

flict with the concept of preservation of the forest was scarcely mentioned. The "recreation" banner was new and bright and had dollar signs on each of its four corners, whereas the cause of a natural reserve for redwoods had an old, tattered ensign, liberally splotched with red ink.

Anyone who has spent much time in the redwood country becomes skeptical about the ability of a vast, untouched redwood forest to provide outdoor recreation for the masses. Old-growth redwood stands, away from the river flats, contain tangled masses of undergrowth covering the remains of giants fallen over past decades, before the onslaught of fire, wind or old age. Sword ferns grow in jungle-like masses taller than a man's head.

Thickets of salal and huckleberry can make progress in any direction almost impossible. The dense redwoods are just not conducive to a quiet forest stroll. During the winter the forest is storm-tossed and dangerous, wet and gloomy, attractive only to the most hardy wilderness seeker. Most public use is confined to the summer, and is likely to continue in this pattern. At any time, however, it is the contrast between dense forest and openings in the form of natural glades, man-made clearings or the successional growth of stream bottoms that is most attractive to the viewer. The denser forests can be opened by road or trail to be made accessible to those visitors who do not wish to risk being tripped or tangled. But the redwood edge is the prime attraction that has been taken advantage of in the river-bottom groves that form the state parks. The redwood edge is also where wildlife is found in variety and abundance. The interior of the old forests supports few kinds of animals, and those that do occur are likely to be high in the trees or living deep in the undergrowth. The Roosevelt elk, black-tailed deer, black bear and most lesser mammals are edge species that thrive in the successional growth of cut-over or burned-over lands. They are not of the old forest interior. Indeed the increase in deer and elk has been in direct relationship to the amount of logging that has taken place.

If one were to devise a redwood park purely for the attraction of the average tourist and the enjoyment of the general public, it would be centered around the river-bottom groves, the seacoast and other areas of natural interspersion, extending to take in some areas of higher country to show off the different kinds of redwood forests that grow on the ridges. A large, continuous block of redwoods is hardly needed for *mass* recreation.

There are, however, good reasons for preserving a large, continuous tract of redwood forest. Such a forest is needed for scientific study, for experimental management, for wilderness recreation and finally just for that indeterminate purpose of diversity, as a large sample of the old America saved for the ages to wonder at.

For scientific purposes, it should be large and continuous, since its value lies in its being an intact biotic community, supporting,

Such a forest is needed for scientific study, for experimental management, for wilderness recreation and finally just for that indeterminate purpose of diversity. (*Humboldt State College photograph by Charles F. Yocom*)

so far as possible, all of the species characteristic of the old, extensive forest. There must be a minimum of man-made edge or disturbance, if one is to study organisms that belong to the intact biota. Such a forest must include entire, undisturbed watersheds to avoid any disruption of its hydrology. It must be, so far as possible, free from all kinds of human disturbance or interference.

Closely associated with the undisturbed forest should be other areas available for experimental management. These might well be arranged as a buffer around an undisturbed core area. Since we do not yet know how to manage a redwood forest in a way that will maintain its health and productivity, these management areas would give us the opportunity to find out. They would permit us to extend our knowledge of the ecology of redwoods.

Combined with the undisturbed area they would be of ever-growing value to the timber industry and to all agencies concerned with the management of redwood areas.

Although neither the intact forest or the management areas could do more than provide a background for areas in which mass recreation was accommodated, they could serve to some degree for limited wilderness recreation. Although only a minority could be allowed to use them, and these only in such ways that would cause no interference with their primary purpose, this minority could benefit from such use. In a world that has

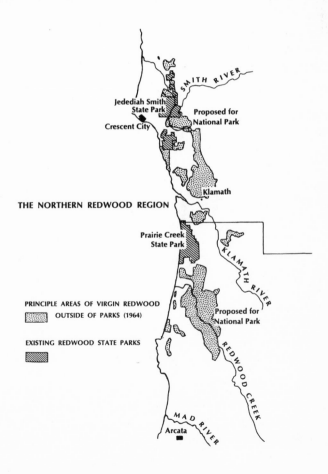

THE NORTHERN REDWOOD REGION

Jedediah Smith State Park

Crescent City

Proposed for National Park

Klamath

Prairie Creek State Park

PRINCIPLE AREAS OF VIRGIN REDWOOD
OUTSIDE OF PARKS (1964)

Proposed for National Park

EXISTING REDWOOD STATE PARKS

SMITH RIVER

KLAMATH RIVER

REDWOOD CREEK

MAD RIVER

Arcata

become far too accessible to the car-traveling, sight-seeing public, the value of areas preserved for the more hardy can be immeasurably great.

There is only one time when such a large block of redwood forest in its primitive state could be set aside and that is the present. Each day that logging continues there is less of it. There is one area in which the best such block of forest remains, the Redwood Creek drainage near Orick, in Humboldt County. Ironically enough, this is not the area finally selected by the National Park Service as the site for the Redwood National Park, although it has been included in various bills introduced in Congress.

The National Park Service has an excellent record in many respects and is staffed by many first-rate people. It is, however, committed to the concepts of preservation and recreation. Although it has in the past sponsored or conducted some first-rate research into wild-land ecology, research has not been its strong feature and has been budgeted inadequately. There is no public agency in existence that is prepared to combine the high degree of preservation, the needed scientific research and management and the development of public recreational space that would be needed in the combination park, management research area and scientific reserve that has been described. The Forest Service has allowed itself to be identified too strongly with commercial utilization; the Bureau of Land Management has been subjected to an overdose of political interference. Any of these federal land-management agencies could do the job if it would broaden its concepts and expand the range of its activities. It would then, however, be suspected of poaching on the preserves of other agencies.

Whether or not a Redwood National Park would bring a great increment of tourist income to the redwood region, the effect of a park on the economy of the region can only be viewed against the question of what would happen to the economy in the absence of a park. This question, of course, has touched off a vast outpouring of contradictory statistics from both sides of the controversy. One company claims it has enough old-growth timber to sustain its activities over a forty-year period.

By then, it has pointed out, it would have sufficient second-growth timber to permit a sustained-yield program indefinitely into the future. To counter this, other arguments show that at the recent rates of cutting the old-growth timber will disappear in relatively few years. The more conservative statistics indicate that within fifteen or twenty years most of the old-growth redwood will have been cut. At that time, if not sooner, the timber-based economy will suffer a severe setback.

There is not enough second-growth redwood in the northwestern California area to sustain the present level of timber-based economic activity. The future of the redwood-region economy, with or without a park, will be bleak as long as a single industry is relied upon to provide the chief support for the area. The situation probably cannot be corrected locally. State and federal attention to the development of a major urbanized area in this region of California is needed for reasons that will be considered in a later chapter. If such a northern city were developed, its inhabitants would place immense value on the redwood park that was preserved in their backyard.

Decisions about our wild lands are now determined by our urban populations. The resources of the wild lands supply the physical needs of city people; the open spaces and living creatures provide recreation and spiritual enrichment. More and more, recreational values are being given first priority by the urbanized majority of Americans. But the cost of providing land for recreation is felt most strongly by the rural counties in which the lands are located. If decisions about land use are to be made in the cities, the costs of those decisions need to be borne by the cities. Rural populations and those in smaller towns need schools, roads, health services, water, waste-removal facilities and all of the same necessities and amenities that city people require. But if rural counties are denied the income from rural lands, then they must be compensated for the income they would have received if the city people had not made the land-use decisions. This is a fact of life that neither state nor federal governments have fully faced. It is a fact that county governments prefer not to face, since most prefer to maintain a maximum degree of independence from the state and the national government. We are reaching a point, however, where rural county governments must be subsidized to a greater degree or the state must take over their functions and provide their services to rural populations.

The redwood controversy thus serves to illustrate many of the factors that face us in attempts to preserve diversity in America. The first and most resistant to rational solution is the deep emotional difference between those who believe strongly in the traditional rights of land ownership and free enterprise and those who recognize a strong degree of public interest in all lands and in the operation of all economic enterprises. Second, and related to the first, is the degree to which local political autonomy depends upon the retention by local citizens of decision-making power over land use. As this is removed the viability of the local political agency is diminished. Next we find a distressing lack of ecological knowledge about many of our most important living resources, and even the lack of an accurate, continuing inventory of our lands and resources. A fourth point is the absence of generally acceptable methods for evaluating the economic impact of proposed changes in the administration of lands, where this involves a shift from the production of tangible goods to the production of more intangible values. Finally, there is the absence of a public land agency with sufficient flexibility in philosophy, policy, administrative and management practice to administer the broad spectrum of land uses from complete wilderness preservation at one extreme to mass recreational use or full economic utilization at the other. All of these factors promote confusion of purpose, and controversy among those who seek to preserve or use the lands and resources of America. They need further exploration here with reference to other lands and other issues.

Apart from the general factors relating to all lands, the redwood controversy is unusual, differing from most national park debates. The old-growth redwood forest is a unique and irreplaceable natural asset that has been disappearing at a rapid rate. Unless the decision has been made to preserve it, before this book appears in print, it may well be too late. Considerations on its use and management are secondary at this moment; we must first stop the logging. We may have no second chance.

5

Fragments of Wilderness

Wilderness is the raw material out of which man has hammered the artifact called civilization.

Wilderness was never a homogeneous raw material. It was very diverse, and the resulting artifacts are very diverse. These differences in the end-product are known as cultures. The rich diversity of the world's cultures reflects a corresponding diversity in the wilds that gave them birth.

—Aldo Leopold

IN AMERICA wilderness is an emotional word. It has developed connotations that combine the primitive and primeval with the virginal and pure. In other, older lands wilderness in the American sense no longer exists and people get by with the changed, although often still wild, lands that remain. In the more recently settled or undeveloped countries wild land is regarded as it was here a century ago, as an obstacle to be overcome, a place to be subdued and settled. Here in the United States our sense of the past, our interest in nature, our desire for outdoor recreation and our concern for outdoor, scientific study areas combine with deep and sometimes irrational emotions to produce attitudes toward wilderness that may defy logical analysis. I do not pretend to be free of such attitudes since the loss of wilderness even in areas that I will never see arouses deep feeling. There is a need, however, to distinguish and separate the various reasons for advocating the preservation of wild areas. Confused emotionalism can result in confused management. Such can lead to the destruction of wilderness.

The old wilderness has vanished from the area bounded by Canada and Mexico. The samples of it that have been saved are precious indeed but should not be confused with the old reality. Qualities of wilderness that were accepted by the pioneer are now lacking, most markedly the qualities of mystery and danger. The old explorers went into land without guideposts or maps. At best they had tales told by the few who had preceded them along the way and had returned. But there were also those who had vanished without word of their fate. When the last settlement was left behind, no agency was there to look after the welfare of the traveler. Behind each mountain range anything might lie. Unknown dangers were a certainty, but there was also the hope of finding something that would make the effort worthwhile. I think the hope of diversity always drove men on, since there would be little joy in exploring an area that was everywhere the same.

Today our wilderness regions are mapped and known. Wilderness travelers are the concern of forest or park rangers who strive to guarantee at least a minimum degree of safety. The adventurer may go to the farthest reaches of the Salmon River high in the Bitterroot Mountains, but no wild Indians will attack him and he will discover no lands that are new. In search of wildness he can take his canoe through the far channels of the Minnesota boundary country, climb to the top of Mount Whitney or venture to the depths of the Everglades. Civilization will be at best a day's journey away.

It would be easy to build a depressing view of how much we have lost of the old wilderness values, but there is a matter of perspective to be considered. Man does not live by realities alone, but by dreams and imagination as well. Sometimes I have felt the qualities of wilderness in places close to home. Dense vegetation such as the chaparral of California discourages visitors. Even

Dense vegetation such as the chaparral of California discourages visitors, preserves a feeling of wilderness in miniature.

the dedicated hunter usually picks the easy routes, up ridges or over rocky soils where the brush thins. After watching one relatively small area of chaparral over a period of five years I decided that there were large portions, one third to one half of the total area, that were apparently unvisited. One could travel a hundred yards from some well-traveled route and be exploring, on a small scale, completely new ground. This was wilderness in miniature located within a few miles of a major summer-resort area, yet there was a thrill of discovery to it. One might find only a wren that had not seen a human face-to-face and displayed too much curiosity for its own safety, or perhaps an owl that had not before been flushed from its roost by a human intruder and flapped off indignantly into still denser cover. One could hope, however, for something more dramatic, a black bear or the last of the local mountain lions. There was even a degree of danger. One who met an accident in a dense brush field might lie a long time without discovery.

The role of dense cover in creating a feeling of wilderness is particularly important in the flat or rolling lands of the East and Middle West. R. C. Lucas investigated the question of wilderness perception in the Minnesota boundary country. He discovered that many people believed they were in wilderness long before the actual wilderness area was reached. A thin screen of untouched forest served to separate them from obvious evidence of human disturbance, such as recently logged-over land. This was enough to produce the feeling of remote and truly wild country.

The aspect of seasonal use of much of our wild country also enters into consideration of wilderness quality. An area full of people from the start of summer until the end of hunting season in autumn may then be suddenly deserted. When the last sporting rifle has fired, solitude returns. Wild animals go back to their normal patterns of feeding, sleeping, breeding or loafing, as though man had never been. If one could ignore the debris left behind by the seasonal visitors, he could sense the wilderness reasserting itself on the land. High mountains have this quality when winter closes the roads with snow and winds whip around the high peaks. Apart from established winter resorts the coun-

When winter closes the roads with snow and winds whip around the peaks—
wilderness returns to the high country.

try becomes as remote and dangerous as in primitive times. Anyone caught far from camp in an unexpected winter storm can
testify to this quality.

Our definition of wilderness in America, however, has become
standardized and we must distinguish between it and land that
is merely wild. In a report prepared for the President's Outdoor
Recreation Resources Review Commission certain criteria were
listed:

1. A wilderness area must be at least one hundred thousand
acres in size, since smaller areas are too likely to be influenced
by the character of the surrounding, modified land. This has
since been adjusted downward, but serves to set the lower limits
for our major wilderness areas.

2. A wilderness area must be a single unit with relatively regular boundaries to preserve its internal integrity and avoid the effects of changes working inward from its edge.

3. An area must show no significant disturbance to plants or animals from human activities. Here, accepting widespread reality, it was necessary to make exceptions. Man's influence has been all-pervasive. Changes induced by the grazing of domestic livestock are excepted. Changes in eastern forests caused by logging in the distant past, where effects have largely disappeared, are excepted. The effects of man's continued efforts at fire suppression are disregarded. The effects brought by the removal of those species of animals that are now extinct or greatly reduced in their distribution are also disregarded since they cannot be repaired. Obviously the more exotic changes wrought by introduced and widespread diseases and parasites, radioactive fallout, pesticide fallout, increased carbon dioxide in the atmosphere and other man-induced global changes are ignored.

4. Finally, the area must be without roads useful to the visiting public. Old mining roads, fire suppression roads and the like are necessarily ignored. It goes without saying that the effects of primitive man over past millennia of land occupancy are also ignored.

The Wilderness Act passed by Congress in 1964 established a national wilderness preservation system (Table 1). The areas included are to be preserved in a roadless and undeveloped state for perpetuity, and are not to be used for any purpose that would modify their primitive, natural state. As is usual, exceptions were made. Mining interests take precedence over God and nature. It was also believed that low intensity grazing did not detract from wilderness quality. Under this act those areas already designated formally as wilderness by the United States Forest Service in the national forests were given formal Congressional protection. Equally wild primitive areas, under national forest management, and smaller wild areas were not blanketed in, nor were wilderness areas that were under the administrative control of other government agencies. All of these were

TABLE 1

Areas Protected by National Wilderness System. 1965.

State	Area	Acreage
Arizona	Mazatzal	205,000
	Superstition	124,140
California	John Muir	502,978
	Marble Mountain	213,283
	Minarets	109,484
	Yolla Bolly	109,051
Idaho	Selway-Bitterroot	987,910
Minnesota	Boundary Waters	786,497
Montana	Anaconda-Pintlar	157,803
	Bob Marshall	950,000
	Selway-Bitterroot	251,930
New Mexico	Gila	483,360
	Pecos	165,000
Oregon	Eagle Cap	216,250
	Three Sisters	196,708
Washington	Glacier Peak	458,105
Wyoming	Bridger	383,300
	South Absaroka	505,552
	North Absaroka	359,700
	Teton	563,460

designated for later study and possible inclusion in the national wilderness system. This study is now going on.

It was determined by the Outdoor Recreation Resources Review Commission that there were a total of sixty-four large wilderness areas left in the forty-eight original states of which only twenty were included in the 1964 act. These areas cover twenty-eight million acres of land, of which more than 80 per cent is located in the high mountains of the West. Only seven areas that approached or exceeded one million acres in size were found to remain. These included one in the Sierra Nevada of California, partly included in the wilderness system; two in the mountains of Idaho, of which one was included; two in the Rockies of Wyoming that were partly included; one in the Montana Rockies that was included; and the Florida Everglades, not yet included. Even these areas are not very large. A traveler proceeding by foot, horseback or boat could not go more than a day's journey from a road or other evidence of man's occupancy of the land.

In addition to the sixty-four large wilderness areas there are at least eighty areas of smaller size that meet most criteria of wilderness. These wild or primitive areas total an additional four million acres of land. The total area of wilderness and smaller wild areas that are under some degree of administrative protection from change make up only 2 per cent of the land area of the contiguous United States. It is sobering to realize that 98 per cent of the land within the nation has disappeared from wilderness status or is in imminent danger of change.

In all the land east of the Rockies only six large wilderness areas remain. Three of these include samples of the northern and eastern coniferous forests of pine, spruce and hemlock: one in the Adirondacks, one on the northern border of Minnesota, the

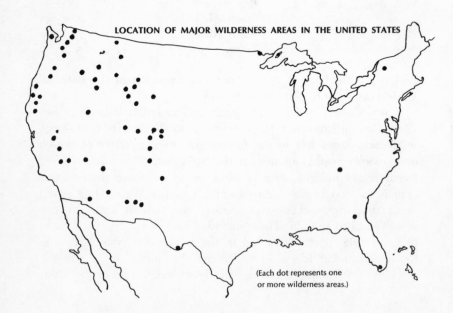

LOCATION OF MAJOR WILDERNESS AREAS IN THE UNITED STATES

(Each dot represents one or more wilderness areas.)

Isle Royale—a wilderness of wolves and moose. (*Photograph courtesy of National Park Service*)

third on Isle Royale in Lake Superior. Two represent the wet-lands of the American Southeast, the wooded swamps of Oke-finokee and the tropical marshes and woods of the Everglades. Only one, the Great Smoky Wilderness of the Carolina-Tennessee border, represents the once vast broad-leaved forest that the pioneers found spreading from the Atlantic to the Mississippi. This is now in danger of being cut in two if the National Park Service goes ahead with its plan for a major highway through it. Most of the original forest of the eastern United States disap-peared without leaving any sizable untouched remnant of the wilderness country that once confronted Audubon or Daniel Boone. In the grasslands that once stretched from the foothills of the Rockies to the prairies of Illinois we have saved no wilderness region.

The area from the Rockies to the Pacific appears in better shape, since here are fifty-eight of the sixty-four wilderness tracts. On closer consideration, however, it will be found that most of these are in the high mountains and preserve only the subalpine fringes of vegetation and the higher mountain coniferous forests. Absent from the western wilderness is any extensive area of grassland or sagebrush. There are no wilderness areas in the chaparral, oak woodland or the once extensive

The Great Smokies—a last remnant of the old eastern wilderness. (*Photograph courtesy of National Park Service*)

marshlands of the Pacific. All areas that had recognizable usefulness were removed from a wilderness condition long before any serious consideration was given to wilderness protection. This does not mean that no natural areas remain in the many vegetation types not included in wilderness areas, but only that these are not of large size. It does not mean that we have no large wild tracts of desert, sagebrush or grassland, but only that these have been modified to a degree that leaves them no longer in a primitive state.

The task of wilderness preservation is more difficult than many realize. The job does not end when we pass a preservation law. Wild country is forever changing. Each year the animals and plants that comprise it are born or grow, decline or die. In no two years will an area be the same. Each community of living things follows pathways determined by soil, weather and the limited ranges of tolerance to change that are an inherited characteristic of each species. Each wilderness area is further affected by the changes that go on in the tamer lands that surround it. The Salmon-Trinity region of California could be a splendid wilderness, but change is encroaching from all sides and it cannot avoid the effects brought by dams, roads and power lines that form part of the state water plan, nor those involved in its ever-growing accessibility to greater numbers of people. The Everglades of Florida are affected by the growth of the Florida urban complex. Increasing populations and increasing leisure affect every wilderness. The growth and spread of cities creates new urban ecosystems that now channel the resources of all America and affect the status of the most remote lands.

Those of us who favor wilderness have yet to face fully the implications of the decision to save it. To keep it we must manage it, although to many the word "management" seems anathema when applied to wilderness. Yet, in a country where all pieces of land fit into somebody's plan, the decision to leave an area alone is a management decision, and its implementation requires effort and planning, from patrolling a boundary to finding some place else for people to go.

If a lightning-caused fire threatens to destroy some area of wilderness forest, most will decide that the fire must be suppressed

The Everglades are just not like any other place. (*Photograph courtesy of National Park Service*)

and controlled. Yet in the Old West it would have burned. The decision to control it interferes with nature and introduces a man-made change into the wilderness. The consequences of this decision could involve the disappearance of those plants and animals that are favored by the recurrence of fire. Similarly, the spread of an insect or disease through a wilderness, killing the trees, usually brings some demand for control. But such control upsets another balance and changes the pattern of wilderness life. Further difficulties are presented by the confusion of purposes among agencies that now administer our wilderness lands and by the activities of those people who are most interested in using these lands.

In the United States areas that remained wild because they were unpublicized and difficult of access are now nationally known. Visitors head toward them. With increasing numbers of visitors, support for their preservation grows. But visitors can trample the wildness out of wilderness. An area visited by great numbers ceases to be wild. Too many feet on a mountain trail leave a lasting scar. Too many packhorses destroy a meadow. The major difficulty in wilderness administration will involve keeping excess numbers of wilderness seekers out.

To consider further aspects of the wilderness conflict, attention will be paid to two major and different wilderness regions, the North Cascades and the Everglades. Each has its own problems. Together they point to some decisions that must be made if wilderness is to be saved.

The word unique has been worked to death, but the Everglades are just not like any place else in the United States. They are located in a state with the longest history of European settlement in the United States, within reach of the bursting metropolis of Miami, yet they remain wild. By any reasonable definition of the tropics, southern Florida is tropical. This is not so much an effect of latitude, since Florida lies well north of the Tropic of Cancer, but rather of the Gulf Stream that brings warm equatorial waters around the Florida peninsula, and of global air movements that direct trade winds toward its shores and bring summer monsoons and at times tropical hurricanes.

The rare wood stork—threatened by man-made drought. (*Photograph courtesy of National Park Service*)

The boundary separating tropical from subtropical is indefinite, but runs approximately from Miami through the southern end of Lake Okeechobee to Naples on the Gulf Coast. Some elements of tropical life extend north of that line and some temperate and subtropical elements extend far south. Along the shore tropical characteristics are shown by the reef-building corals that have formed the keys that border Biscayne Bay and extend southward to form the southern boundary of Florida Bay. Farther inshore the mangrove swamps that line the muddy shores are tropical. Mangroves, corals and other marine organisms have worked together to build sea into land and create the Florida peninsula in the shape that it exhibits today.

The Florida panther is still common in the Everglades. (*Photograph courtesy of National Park Service*)

Still farther inland the plants of the hammock forests are those of the tropical West Indies, with their centers of distribution lying in the islands to the south. The great saw grass marshes, the Everglades proper, are themselves tropical in nature. The region supports animal life that includes the rare Everglades kite, a hawk that feeds on snails; the anhinga, a diving bird with a long, snake-like neck; the spectacular roseate spoonbill; the rare wood stork; the alligators and crocodiles of the inland waterways and estuaries; the manatees of the bays and inlets.

The glades are interspersed with hammock forests in which tropical vegetation dominates. (*Photograph courtesy of National Park Service*)

The aquatic life that supports a multi-million dollar fishing industry is itself tropical in nature.

The climate of the region is of the two-season, dry, tropical variety. The dry season that extends from November to April is part of the present Everglades problem. It gives rise to a different type of tropical environment than that found in America's other tropical state, Hawaii. This tropical environment and the biota that it supports have long been of interest to biologists. To people in general they provide a diversity of environment and a quality to life that should not be sacrificed to expediency. For a long time tropical Florida, inland from the Atlantic coast, was an unusually wild and remote area, spared from the encroachment of civilization by its inhospitable swamps and mazes of waterways. Today this is no longer true. Civilization has pushed up to the boundaries of the one extensive wild area that remains, Everglades National Park. Its presence creates doubt that even the million and a half acres set aside for preservation "for all time" will be large enough to resist the changes imposed from outside.

The vegetation of America's tropical wilderness is dominated by the Everglades themselves. These are a tropical fresh-water marsh in which a tall species of sedge known as saw grass (*Cladium jamaicensis*) is dominant. This forms a barrier to travel in itself since it grows up to ten feet high and is armed with sharp edges to its grass-like blades. Growing with the saw grass are true grasses as well as broad-leaved plants, but saw grass is most prevalent. The surface on which they grow is limestone rock covered by a layer of limy marl. This is eroded by rainfall and the acids from decomposing vegetation into an uneven surface, pitted with deep sinkholes in places, and with larger ponds and sloughs that hold water through the year and provide a refuge for alligators and fish along with water birds and other aquatic animals during the dry season. This broken surface, however, adds to difficulties of travel across what appears at first glance to be a level prairie. The Everglades once formed a broad arc from Lake Okeechobee southward to where they meet the salt marshes and mangroves that form the western and southern border of Florida. Once they occupied

The larger sloughs hold water through the year and give a home to alligators.

an area forty miles wide by eighty miles long. Today the area that remains in the national park is less than half of the original.

The Everglades, however, are defined not just by marsh grassland, but by their bay heads or hammocks. These are areas of slightly higher ground, not subject to flooding, that support plants that cannot stand submergence of their roots or stems. Elevation is the key to vegetation zonation in the Everglades as in the mountains of the West; but in the Everglades elevations are measured in inches and in the western mountains in thousands of feet. A few inches of soil above the level that is seasonally flooded can make a great difference in Florida vegetation. On the hammocks grow forests typical of the West Indian region. Trees may include such species as the conspicuous gumbo-limbo with its reddish, peeling, naked-looking bark; the poisonous manchineel, the sap of which can inflict a rash more serious than poison ivy; the custard apple, lignum vitae, tropical mahogany and the often unwelcome strangler figs that enclose and cut off the trees that have sheltered and supported their seeds and seedlings. These trees will often support a

Paurotis palm

Royal palm

Mahogany

Gumbo limbo

Strangler fig

Epiphytes on cypress. (*Photograph courtesy of National Park Service*)

variety of epiphytes or air plants other than the young strangler figs. These, perched high on branches or trunks, include various colorful orchids, bromeliads with leaves like pineapples, and smaller ferns and mosses. Joining with the broad-leaved trees are various palms, including the towering royal palm, the cabbage palm and the paurotis palm. Where not disturbed the hammocks may develop into tall, relatively open and well-shaded groves dominated by tall mahoganies or live oaks. More often, where hurricane or fire have had their influences, a dense jungle-like growth of younger trees and shrubs will prevail. Toward the northern part of the tropical region, trees more typical of subtropical forests begin to dominate on the hammocks. These include the showy magnolia and the red bay along with the live oak.

To the east of the main Everglades a limestone ridge of low elevation cuts off the swamps from the ocean. Before the developers arrived this supported a tropical pine forest dominated by Caribbean pine in open stands with an understory including cabbage palm and saw palmetto. Part of this is preserved in the national park, but the loggers got there first. Only second growth remains. In time, barring further disturbance, the old-

Pines grown on the higher limestone ridges, where fires are frequent.

growth pine forest will return to the park. Outside the park there seems little hope for the remnants that are left.

Over most of the western and southern coast of Florida, mangroves dominate the strip between land and sea. Unlike most trees, mangroves are halophytes, meaning they have a high degree of tolerance for salt water. Since the degree of tolerance varies with the different species of mangroves, a zonation of the mangrove swamps can often be observed, from the ocean or bay side inland to where they are replaced on dry ground by hammock forests.

Mangroves are land builders, since they accumulate not only the debris of their own dead leaves, branches and trunks, but also materials washed in by the tide. In building land, however, they make the area less suited to their own presence and permit its invasion by dry-land vegetation. The zonation in a mangrove swamp thus illustrates the process of biotic succession, the replacement of one plant community by another until a final, relatively stable, climax form of vegetation is reached. In the mangroves this replacement runs from those species most tolerant to salt and to partial submersion to those less tolerant.

The seaward fringe of mangroves is occupied by the red mangrove (*Rhizophora mangle*), which dominates from the mean tide level out as far as the mean low-tide level, beyond which the muddy floor of the sea is not often exposed. This species develops prop roots which enable it to resist the ebb and

Mangroves dominate the south and west of the national park. (*Photograph courtesy of National Park Service*)

Red mangroves, with their stilt-like prop roots, pioneer the way to form new land.

Black mangroves, characterized by the root projections that extend up from the ground, follow the red mangroves in invading new ground.

flow of the tide and the force of waves. The roots often interlace to form a network difficult to pass through. The seeds of this plant germinate on the tree and develop an elongated tap root before they fall to the ground. Once fallen they may plant themselves in the mud below, or be carried by the tide out to some exposed mud bar where the root can penetrate and the young tree grow.

Above the level of mean tide the black mangrove (*Avicennia nitida*) replaces the red. Since it is protected from the force of moving water it does well without prop roots. However, since it grows in mud saturated with water, aeration of its roots presents a problem. This is solved by the development of pneumatophores, erect aerial roots that grow up from below the mud and provide channels for distribution of air within the root system. Along with the prop roots of the red mangrove, the erect roots of the black add to the difficulty of traversing a mangrove swamp.

The inward fringe of the black mangrove zone may be occupied by a third species, the white mangrove (*Laguncularia*). Still farther inland, above the mean high-tide line, is a zone of button-mangrove or buttonwood (*Conocarpus*). This mixes with

Mangrove swamps form a nearly impenetrable tangle.

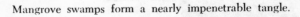

or is replaced by the climax, hammock type of tropical forest. The animal life of mangrove swamps is often abundant. Oysters and marine snails may be numerous among the partially sub-merged stems and roots, along with great herds of mud-dwelling crabs. Insects abound. Sea birds and marsh birds, including pelicans, cormorants, terns, and the various herons, egrets, spoon-bills and storks, roost in the trees.

The seaward march of land and of land vegetation that is pioneered by the advance of the outer fringe of red mangroves is not without setbacks and interruptions. At intervals severe storms or hurricanes will sweep in from the ocean, hurling sea water high over the land, sweeping living trees, soil and debris alike back into the sea until such time as the waves or tides carry it landward once more to start anew the process of land building and colonization. In 1935 a hurricane killed out a large area of mangroves in the Everglades National Park. The 1960 Hurricane

Hurricanes do great damage, strip leaves and branches from trees, some-times destroy whole forests.

Donna did an amazing amount of damage to the national park, stripping the leaves from the royal palms in Royal Palm hammock, uprooting the ancient mahoganies in Mahogany hammock and killing most of the park's mangroves. New growth came in only to be hit once more by Hurricane Betsy in 1965. However, hurricanes build land as well as tear it down, piling soil and plant seeds in new areas. They are a factor to which life in the Florida tropics has become adapted, and were it not for man's influence also acting on the same environment, they would not be a cause for concern.

It was not the mangroves, the tropical woodlands or the marshes that attracted people to southern Florida. Instead the winter climate of blue skies and warm sunshine combined with the broad white beaches of seashore and coral key to become an irresistible lure to those who lived in stormy, snow-swept regions. Florida became vacation land, retirement land, and then, as a gateway to tropical America, a center of commerce and industry. Settlement clustered at first along the coast, spreading inland only on higher ground. But the demand for land became too great, and efforts were made to control the waters and create useful land in the interior. Dams, ditches and canals made possible the spread of farm and urban land into the former wetlands and brought the threat of complete loss of the Florida wilderness. Realizing the danger, Congress acted to establish Everglades National Park by passing a bill authorizing the park in 1934. It was not until 1947, however, that sufficient land purchases had been made inside the park boundary to give the necessary unity and control to the park, and in that year the park was finally dedicated and opened. The final park was not as large as had been authorized, but it was all that the government felt it could afford to buy.

It is one thing to set aside a national park and another thing to hold it in a land beset by hurricane, fire, drought and ever-growing numbers of people. Congress, in setting aside the park, failed to provide one essential for the park's survival—access to fresh water.

The Everglades were formed originally in the drainage path from Lake Okeechobee. The lake collected storm and flood waters

Development spreads in southern Florida, threatening the future of all wild areas. (*Photograph courtesy of National Park Service*)

The Everglades have been dependent on a southward flow of water from Lake Okeechobee through the marshes, creating the "river of grass" effect. Without adequate water the glades and all of their remarkable inhabitants will not survive. (*Photograph courtesy of National Park Service*)

from much of central Florida and helped maintain a southward flow of this water through the Everglades, creating the "river of grass" effect in this marsh. This flow of fresh water, moving on the surface and through the porous limestone rock beneath the surface, kept the ground saturated in southern Florida and prevented invasion of salt water from the ocean. At times, during periods of drought, the Everglades would dry out and burn over, but the frequency of fire under primitive conditions would have been low. Flooding through much of the year prevented the invasion of woody vegetation except for those trees and shrubs able to withstand submersion. Burning during the drought period killed back those woody plants that had managed to invade and thus kept the grass-like vegetation dominant. The higher hammocks were mostly protected by surrounding sloughs and sinks from fires that swept quickly over the lower-lying grasslands, and thus continued to support woody vegetation.

The normal flow of water in southern Florida was first interrupted when drainage projects began to reclaim the marshes and permit the establishment of agricultural and residential land use. In the 1920s the new settlements were endangered when hurricanes and drenching rains caused Lake Okeechobee to overflow its banks and floodwaters to smash homes and take hundreds of human lives. Following this, canals were built from the lake eastward to the Atlantic and westward along the Caloosahatchee River to the Gulf. These drained the excess lake water that had previously flowed southward. However, hurricanes and floods hit again in the 1940s with more damage. The United States Corps of Engineers responded to local demand by constructing a new series of levees and canals that enabled the level of Lake Okeechobee to be lowered before the start of the rainy season. Excess water from the lakes was stored in three large pools called "conservation areas" lying south of the lake. From these, waters could be released to agricultural areas or residential use along the coast. This construction effectively cut off all regular flow to Everglades National Park. The flood control and water storage works were built with federal funds, but the federal interest in the national park was not recognized. Instead, control over water distribution was given to the Central and Southern Florida

Flood Control District, an agency under state and local authority. The Everglades began to suffer from drought, which was accentuated during the dry years of 1961 to 1967.

Even during drought years water was available within Lake Okeechobee that could have been released to the park. The park was in dire need of water. Marshlands were drying, aquatic animals and birds were dying from lack of habitat, salt water was invading along the coast, killing off the creatures that needed brackish or fresh water. During the 1964–65 season, one species of rare bird, the wood stork, had its production of young cut to 5 per cent of normal. With loss of adults and little replacement from young the species was threatened with extinction. However, rather than make any concessions to the park or reach any standing agreement to supply water to it, as much as 1,500,000 acre-feet of water were released from Lake Okeechobee directly into the ocean during the years 1963 to 1965. The water could have made a vast difference to the park, but the developers and speculators of southern Florida wanted no commitment that might interfere with their future plans for land use outside the park.

The Everglades require a minimum of 250,000 acre-feet of water flowing through the park and normally would benefit by a flow of 400,000 acre-feet. The park cannot meet these needs within its own boundaries. The flow must go through the Everglades and into the sea in order to maintain the proper salinities and conditions for life in estuaries and prevent invasion of seawater.

In 1965 the pressure from conservationists and the National Park Service forced one concession from the state of Florida. The Park Service was authorized to tap underground water supplies in the Biscayne aquifer, within the park. From this, some 73,000 acre-feet of water could be pumped into the park. By 1966, however, it was obvious that there was a need for much more. Faced with ever-growing national concern for the fate of the park and pressure from its own tourist-based economic interests, the state authorities, flood control district and Corps of Engineers agreed to bring water once more from Lake Okeechobee to the park. A million and a half dollars were provided

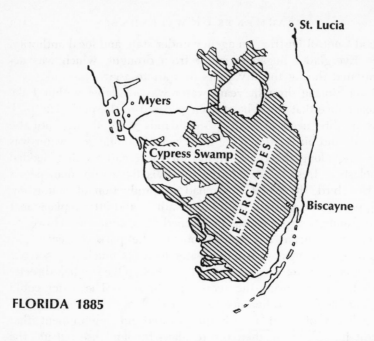

FLORIDA 1885

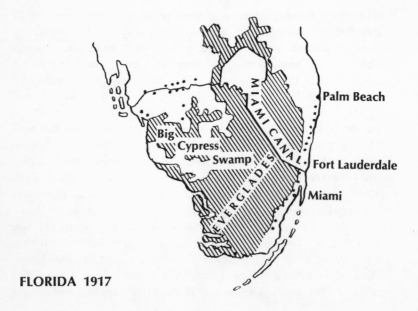

FLORIDA 1917

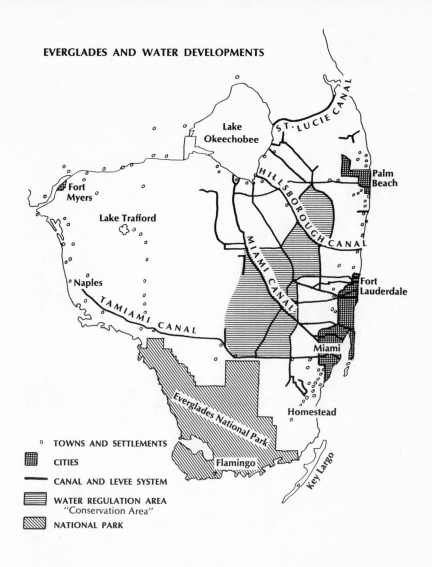

EVERGLADES AND WATER DEVELOPMENTS

Lake Okeechobee

ST·LUCIE CANAL

HILLSBOROUGH CANAL

MIAMI CANAL

TAMIAMI CANAL

Fort Myers

Lake Trafford

Naples

Palm Beach

Fort Lauderdale

Miami

Homestead

Everglades National Park

Flamingo

Key Largo

° TOWNS AND SETTLEMENTS

CITIES

CANAL AND LEVEE SYSTEM

WATER REGULATION AREA
"Conservation Area"

NATIONAL PARK

Maps showing development of canals and levees in Florida: 1885, 1917, 1965.

Whether wilderness and metropolis can exist side by side in Florida has yet to be decided.

to the Corps of Engineers to reopen and enlarge two canals and install the pumps necessary to move the fresh water. What seemed a victory, however, was once more thrown into doubt by the severe 1967 drought. In May, 1967, with both the park and the surrounding areas suffering from the effects of an unusually long dry season, the governor of Florida decided to shut off the new flow of water from the storage areas to the north.

The population of southern Florida continues to grow and demands for water grow with it. The future is uncertain. Former park superintendent William B. Roberston has written: "In the past 40 years, the Everglades has been hurt by drainage and fire. It's a scarred and dog-eared sort of wilderness, but it has great powers of recovery. Fire and extreme variation of water levels have always been characteristic elements of its ecology, and, in a sense, the man-caused disturbances have been no more than nature intensified. . . . Within the next decade we should know whether Everglades water can be managed to permit the peaceful coexistence of wilderness and metropolis in South Florida."

It should be noted that no part of the Everglades is yet in the national wilderness preservation system. The future of the wilderness within the park rests upon administrative decisions of the Park Service until Congress decides upon the fate of this area. If the decision is made to open it up for more intensive tourist use, much of the wilderness quality may be lost even though the water problem be solved. However, this is a secondary concern at present. The Everglades present, along with the redwoods, the more classical conservation struggle in which the interests of private profit conflict with public goals. In such a battle the finer points of wilderness conservation always seem less important.

It is different with the North Cascades. Here the conflict is of a

The North Cascades. Some of the grandest, wildest, most remote country. (*Photograph courtesy of National Park Service*)

different nature and throws light on the agencies that administer wild lands and upon the public that demands both its preservation and its accessibility.

The North Cascades Range of Washington includes some of the grandest, wildest, most remote country south of Canada. Some of its mountains have been called the American Alps, but the Alps are tame by comparison. The remote quality of these mountains is enhanced by their continuation northward into the wild mountains of British Columbia. As yet the region is crossed by no highway north of U.S. 2, which runs from Everett to Wenatchee. However, state highway 20 is biting ever deeper into the region and soon will connect Bellingham with Okanagon. The rubber-tired tourist will have access to land that was once reserved to the wilderness traveler. This highway connection is only part of the invasion of civilization into this once remote area. It goes on under the banner of progress and mostly without protest from any agency or organization.

The quality of the wild country in the valleys and mountains of the North Cascades is enhanced by a great variety in animal life. Here is one of the few areas in the United States where the white mountain goat is relatively common. One may at least hope to encounter those rare and large members of the weasel family, the wolverine and the fisher, in the upper fringes of the timbered country, or higher in the alpine fields. The Canada lynx and cougar are still here and add distinction to the land. It is possible that the rare California bighorn may still appear in the mountains near the Canadian border. Since the connections to Canada are unbroken, one can hope to encounter the stray wolf or grizzly. Among the game birds one finds unusual variety, from the white-tailed ptarmigan of the highest mountain peaks to the spruce grouse of the lodgepole pine forests. The blue grouse and ruffed grouse are more common.

The area that has been subject to administrative controversy and argument among conservationists extends from Mount Rainier north to Canada. In addition to Mount Rainier, the highest volcanic peak south of Canada, the area includes the volcanic cone of Mount Baker on the far north, a landmark on the skyline from Victoria or Vancouver. Both volcanoes were active as recently as 1870 and show signs of continued life. Volcanoes, however, are not the strong feature of the region. The geologically complex rocks are marked by saw-toothed ridges, sheer cliffs, jagged peaks and deeply incised valleys, including those with long, narrow, ribbon lakes and reservoirs, Chelan, Ross and Baker Lakes, for example. There are over five hundred active glaciers in the area, one of the largest sections of alpine, above-timberline scenery to be found west of the Rockies. Here too are forests of subalpine fir and mountain hemlock, rain forests of western red cedar, western hemlock and Douglas fir on the wet western slopes of the mountains, and dry, open ponderosa pine and Douglas fir on the eastern slopes. Nobody questions the value of this region, nor that its quality is equal to any contained in any national park. The question of who should administer it, and how, remains.

Most of the land is under the control of the United States Forest Service in the Department of Agriculture. In the south the 241,000 acre Mount Rainier National Park was cut out of

The bighorn may still appear in the mountains near the Canadian border. (*Photograph courtesy of James D. Yoakum*)

Mount Rainier. (*Photograph courtesy of National Park Service*)

the then Forest Reserves by act of Congress in 1899. It came
under the jurisdiction of the National Park Service when that
agency was formed in the Department of the Interior in 1916.
Most of the land has been under one form of government control
or another since 1846 when the Oregon Territory was taken over
by the United States, and its unclaimed land became part of the
American public domain.

In the 1920s, under the guidance of such men as Aldo Leopold,
the Forest Service developed an interest in the preservation of
wilderness, as such, without development. In 1929 regulations to
permit the establishment of a system of roadless, primitive areas
were put into effect. In 1931 and 1935 an area of 801,000 acres
lying east of Mount Baker and north of where highway 20 will
cross the Cascades was established as a primitive area and maintained in a largely undisturbed state. In 1939 the Forest Service
regulations permitted the establishment of wilderness areas, under stricter control than the older primitive areas. In the North
Cascades, the 458,000 acre Glacier Peak Wilderness Area was

In the Glacier Peak wilderness. (*Photograph courtesy of National Park Service*)

established in 1960. The Wilderness Preservation Act of 1964 brought Glacier Peak into the national wilderness system.

However, there are those who do not trust the Forest Service and believe that wild country is more effectively preserved when it has been given the status of a national park. Starting as far back as 1906 a proposal was made to include part of the more spectacular scenery in the North Cascades in a national park. Since then, such proposals have come with ever-growing frequency and such conservation organizations as the Sierra Club have mounted full-scale drives toward creation of a new national park in the North Cascades.

The North Cascades have therefore brought into opposition the two most powerful conservation agencies in the federal government, and the two federal departments, Agriculture and Interior, most concerned with land conservation matters. Unfortunately these two have been in conflict many times during the history of America, since they represent conflicting phi-

The Picket Range, in the North Cascades Primitive Area. (*Photograph courtesy of National Park Service*)

losophies of land use and conservation. The National Park Service, in Interior, has long been identified with complete preservation, public recreation and public education in the appreciation of nature. Trees that grow in national parks will not be logged by private industry, although they may fall before the demands of the recreationist. Wild animals in the parks are never hunted by the public, although fish may be hunted and killed quite legally. Grasses that grow in the meadows of the parks may not be grazed by privately owned cows or sheep, although they may be killed out by the grazing of pack stock or riding horses used for recreation.

The Forest Service, in Agriculture, has inherited the mantle of Gifford Pinchot, and represents a philosophy of conservation through use. The national forests that it administers were created to protect timber and water for public use. The Forest Service has always placed emphasis on the controlled harvest of national forest timber by private lumber companies, of national forest forage by private livestock and national forest wildlife by the hunting public. The existing policy of the Forest Service was formalized in 1960 by the passage of a multiple use-sustained yield act by Congress which stated that the national forests were to be used for many purposes in such a way as to guarantee a sustained yield of their resources into the future. Among the purposes for which the forests might be used, the preservation of wilderness was recognized.

The National Park Service has acted successfully over the years in having established through act of Congress national parks from national forest land. The Forest Service has resented the transfer of land under its administration to the jurisdiction of another agency. As a result of this and other differences, relationships between the Departments of Interior and Agriculture have not always been cordial. In 1962, however, the secretaries of the two departments announced a new era of cooperation and pledged that inter-agency raids would cease. As part of the new spirit of good will, a joint study of one major area of controversy, the North Cascades, was proposed. In 1963 a joint study team was appointed. It was made up of two representatives of Agriculture, including the Forest Service, two representatives of Interior, including the Park Service, and one neutral, the director of the newly formed Bureau of Outdoor Recreation, who served as chairman. After a two and a half year study the team issued its report in 1965. Interestingly enough the team came to three different conclusions, one representing the viewpoint of the chairman, and two representing minority reports from Interior and Agriculture. The new spirit of cooperation had brought little spirit of compromise.

The Forest Service has long been suspect by many conservation groups because of its apparently too great concern with the production of timber for commercial use. It also antagonized those who believe in wilderness preservation by its opposition to the wilderness preservation bill before its enactment. Nevertheless, in the North Cascades controversy, the Forest Service emerged as the only consistent and determined defender of the wilderness concept. The Bureau of Outdoor Recreation is too new to have a clear public image. In the North Cascades issue the director

Mount Stuart wilderness area. (*Photograph courtesy of National Park Service*)

showed little sympathy for wilderness concepts and placed great emphasis on the need for opening wild country to mass public recreation. The Park Service, longtime favorite of wilderness lover and nature preservationist, emerged with no clear stand on the wilderness question, and left a feeling that its sympathies were on the side of mass public use.

At stake in the North Cascades study were several different issues. First and most controversial was the question of whether a new national park should be created. Second was the fate of the North Cascades Primitive Area, one of the nation's largest wilderness tracts. Third, the question of who should administer the Glacier Peak Wilderness Area. Fourth was the future of a large area known as the Eldorado Peaks High Country, separating Glacier Peak from the North Cascades Primitive Area. Several other areas were also in question, including the future of the public recreation area around Mount Baker. The recommendations of the Study Team are presented in Table 2.

TABLE 2

Comparison of Proposals. North Cascade Study Team.

Team Proposals (Director, Bureau of Outdoor Recreation)	Park Service Proposals	Forest Service Proposals
Establish Okanogon Wilderness from part of North Cascades Primitive Area east of Ross Lake (495,000 acres).	Same as team proposal.	Establish North Cascades Wilderness Area of 813,000 acres.
Establish North Cascades National Park from Eldorado Peaks area and west section of North Cascades Primitive Area. Park to include dams, etc., on Ross and Diablo Lakes. Park to develop public access to Picket Range Wilderness.	Establish two national parks, one around Glacier Peak, other to include Mount Baker Recreation Area and Picket Range section of North Cascades Primitive Area. Place Eldorado Peaks in National Recreation Area.	No national parks. Maintain Eldorado Peaks as recreation area. Leave Picket Range in North Cascades Wilderness without mass recreation access.
Continue Mount Baker as Forest Service Recreation Area.	Change Mount Baker to national park.	Same as team proposal.
Enlarge Glacier Peak Wilderness to include additional 39,000 acres.	Change Glacier Peak area to national park.	Essentially same as team proposal.
Establish Alpine Lakes Wilderness Area of 150,000 acres and Enchantment Wilderness of 30,000 acres.	Establish combined Alpine Lakes and Enchantment Wilderness Area.	Same as team proposal.
Establish Mount Aix Wilderness Area of 45,000 acres.	No recommendation.	Same as team proposal.

Return Cougar Lake and Monte Cristo Peak Limited Areas to multiple-use status.	Add Cougar Lake area to Mount Rainier National Park.	Same as team proposal.
Add southern extension to Mount Rainier National Park.	Same as team proposal plus Cougar Lake extension.	Same as team proposal.

Both the National Park Service and the Bureau of Outdoor Recreation were willing to dismember the North Cascades Primitive Area. The B.O.R. recommendation favored a major road up the shore of Ross Lake across the wilderness, and mass recreational access by helicopter, tramway, funicular or narrow-gauge railway to the now remote Picket Range area of this wilderness. The Park Service favored putting the Picket Range in one of its national parks with no guarantee that its wilderness qualities would be preserved. Only the Forest Service favored addition of the North Cascades Primitive Area in its entirety to the national wilderness preservation system. The Park Service favored creation of a new national park encompassing the Glacier Peak Wilderness Area without showing how the public interest would benefit by transfer to its administration of an area already fully protected by the Wilderness Act. The Park Service also favored creation of a new national park in the Mount Baker area although the recreational facilities already developed in this area go far beyond those normally allowed within national parks.

The reaction of the various private conservation organizations to the North Cascades report was largely predictable. The Sierra Club maintained its suspicion of the Forest Service and belief that national parks are by nature good, even though it was shaken by the proposed mass recreation emphasis for existing wilderness lands. The Wilderness Society showed a good grasp of reality by recommending that all of the wilderness areas be included in the national wilderness preservation system before any agency be allowed to affect their status.

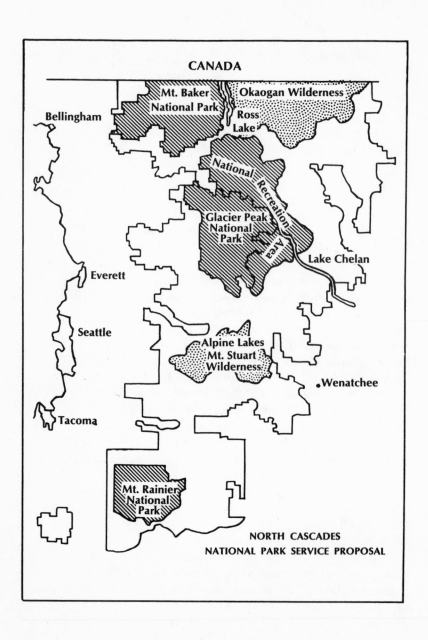

CANADA

Bellingham

Mt. Baker
National Park

Okaogan Wilderness

Ross
Lake

National Recreation Area

Glacier Peak
National
Park

Lake Chelan

Everett

Seattle

Alpine Lakes
Mt. Stuart
Wilderness

•Wenatchee

Tacoma

Mt. Rainier
National
Park

NORTH CASCADES
NATIONAL PARK SERVICE PROPOSAL

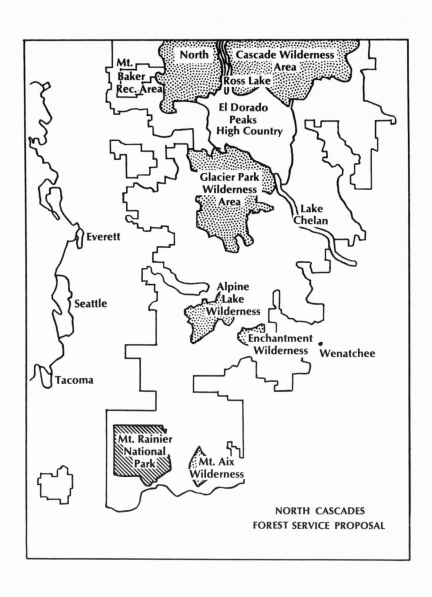

Mt.
Baker
Rec. Area

North   Cascade Wilderness
                Area

Ross Lake

El Dorado
Peaks
High Country

Glacier Park
Wilderness
Area

Lake
Chelan

Everett

Alpine
Lake
Wilderness

Seattle

Enchantment
Wilderness   Wenatchee

Tacoma

Mt. Rainier
National
Park

Mt. Aix
Wilderness

NORTH CASCADES
FOREST SERVICE PROPOSAL

Pressure for a North Cascades National Park will continue and it is possible that the 90th Congress will enact the President's recommendation that one be created. It is hoped however that the National Park Service will clarify its position toward the subject of wilderness preservation before any more of the nation's wildest lands are placed under its administration. It is fortunate that serious inroads on the wilderness of this region are proceeding at a slow pace. If the North Cascades were faced with the crisis that besets the redwoods or Everglades, inter-agency disputes and confusion of purposes could be tragic.

The present Secretary of the Interior, Stewart L. Udall, will go down in history as one of the strongest and most capable advocates of conservation in American government. But he heads a difficult agency which includes in the Bureau of Reclamation one of the outstanding foes of most conservationists, and in the National Park Service one of the best friends. Consequently in recent years the Department has appeared ambiguous on many issues. Thus confusion has arisen about the future of Olympic National Park and its superb wilderness, the future of Great Smoky National Park and the future of the Grand Canyon. Thus far none of these areas has been hurt and the Grand Canyon issue has been resolved in favor of the national park. It will remain difficult, however, to keep Interior moving always in the direction of preserving quality and diversity in the environment.

It is unfortunate that the Forest Service has allowed itself to become identified so closely with "big timber" and the philosophy that the only good tree is a dead one on its way to the mill, or a young one growing board feet for the nation's industries. The many good policies and activities of the Forest Service are often obscured by past deeds and the overstaffing of the service with industry-oriented forestry school graduates.

The nation's wildest lands are the foundation of diversity in America. It is long past time to have a hard look at our policies for their preservation. We are too close to the end of the line for America's wilderness country to allow ambiguity in attitude or blind faith in any conservation agency to continue to operate.

6

The Wilder Reaches

Out on the wastes of the Never Never—
That's where the dead men lie!
                    —Barcroft Henry Boake

A F E W years ago my wife and I paid a visit to Volcán Irazú. After a long period of quiescence this mountain had begun acting up shortly before we arrived in Costa Rica, and the streets of San José were covered each day by a thin layer of volcanic ash. Yet the eruptions had not been spectacular and for some time before our ascent the mountain had been relatively quiet. There was some activity deep within the crater, but nothing was being thrown over the rim. The summit of Irazú is on the rim of the outer crater, formed by some outstanding eruption of long ago. One descends from this several hundred feet to reach the rims of two small inner craters. One contained a lake of a color I can only describe as ghastly green. The other, larger crater was much deeper, and within it, well over one hundred feet below its rim, was the lip of a still smaller crater, the one formed by the eruption that was then taking place.

During the long period when the volcano had been quiet a road was built up over the outer rim and down to the edge of the larger of the inner craters. On this edge a restaurant was constructed where tourists could sit and sip coffee while looking at the evidences of volcanic activity in the depths below. The road, or what was left of it, descended steeply from the outer rim to cross a flat plain and then ascend slightly to the point where the ruins of the restaurant were located. When we were there the landscape was desolate indeed. The flat plain was spattered by volcanic bombs thrown up from the recent eruptions. Everywhere a layer of ash, a foot or more in depth, lay over the land, covering and killing out the dense, heath-like vegetation that had grown on the outer rim; piling up on fence posts and roads, and converting the latter to slippery tracks. Irazú had been no wilderness before its eruption. Dairy farms extended to near the top. But the ranches had become deserted and the people had moved away. Most evidences of man and of life were being removed from the mountaintop. Nature, in its most forbidding aspect, was reclaiming lost ground, creating something beyond mere wilderness, a moon landscape in a forsaken world.

I had been intrigued and attracted by all this. Some ten days

earlier my first fear of the volcano had been overcome when I
went to its top with a group of scientists from a number of
American countries. From the ruins of the old restaurant we
looked down at the new crater and were rewarded with a mild
eruption. It was largely contained within the rim and alarmed
nobody but those who knew the volcano well. The rest of us
looked on with interest as the smoke ascended and volcanic
bombs whizzed through the air well below us.

It was a pleasant enough day when Beth and I arrived at the
top of the outer rim. No people were to be seen, the clouds had
lifted and blue sky was visible. Below us in the inferno world
of the crater was only a faint wisp of steam to show it was still
alive. We trudged down the trail, stopped to look at the small
lake and take a photograph or two, and then moved up to the rim
of the larger inner crater, where we hoped to get a good view
of the recently active interior pit.

But the gods of volcanoes are a fickle lot and somewhere along
the line we had said or done the wrong thing. No sooner did we
look down at the interior crater than it seemed to start moving up
toward us. For seconds I thought it would be a mild little display,
such as I had witnessed before, and I felt cheered at the cooperation the mountain was extending to us. But the smoke and the
ash did not stay down—it kept boiling up toward us. Realizing
we were too close, we ran back down toward the plain. By then
we realized that anywhere was too close. The earth was shaking
beneath our feet and the smell of brimstone was in the air. A
glance back was enough to bring sheer horror. The blue sky
was gone, a black cloud towered above and moved over us so
that we could see lightning flash overhead and the streaks of the
flying bombs. A complete hopelessness hit me as we ran as fast
as we could, expecting momentarily to be struck with molten
rock, to be overcome by fumes or to have the earth fall away beneath us.

At eleven thousand feet our wind was short and we moved
across the plain with all the efficient speed of a mud turtle
crossing a freeway. Miraculously, it seemed, we reached the
point where the road climbed the outer rim and hope gave us
new strength. Halfway up we realized we had a chance if our

hearts would only keep pumping. Then with relief we saw a human being and knew we could be pulled over the top. By then the ash from the eruption towered many thousands of feet in the air and was moving away from us to fall once more on the coffee *fincas*, the rooftops and the streets of San José.

When we could speak we found we had been met by a guard whose job it was to keep people from taking unnecessary risks around the volcano. We assured him there were no other people in the blackness that obscured the scene below us, and we started the long hike downhill to our car, hoping that Irazú would not blow up completely before we left it behind. As we finally drove away I remembered the old story of Mount Pelée on Martinique and the fate that had overcome tens of thousands when the city of Saint Pierre was blotted out by Pelée's eruption. Even San José felt none too safe after that, as each day the ash rained down.

In retrospect I realize that this was a wilderness experience of a kind that is fortunately denied most of us today, but once was common. The forces of nature sometimes strike in blizzard or hurricane, tidal wave, volcano or earthquake, in strength sufficient to make us realize that all is not benign and the world is not entirely bland. They bring into focus fear in its most elemental, basic sense—a fear far different from the gnawing anxiety that besets so many of us who call ourselves civilized.

People who seek out true wilderness are those who do not feel adverse to encounters with nature in its most threatening aspects, who appreciate the sense of awe and wonder that goes with it. I think they must inevitably like the edge of the sea on a stormy day when the surf batters the rocks, and appreciate a hard rain hitting the face as one walks a lonely path. A feeling of the relative insignificance of man compared with the vastness of the universe cannot appall them. Like the bushmen of Africa they are prepared to accept a lesser role on earth and concede first place in the scheme of things to the lion or the elephant.

But wilderness has its more sunny aspect. To me this is always associated with wilderness animal life. I recall one hike through the Olympics, following the crest of a ridge from which I could

A marmot appeared—obviously shocked by the sight of me.

see no sign of humanity. Something about the terrain and the weather combined to bring a feeling of despondency that even the bright fields of alpine wild flowers could not dispel. But then a marmot appeared on the trail ahead who was quite obviously shocked by the sight of me. Caught between two burrows he looked both pathetic and foolish and could not realize the cheer he was bringing to a fellow mammal. From then on the day was brighter, the sun felt warmer, other animals began to appear and the wilderness came alive with chipmunks and birds.

I feel a particular kinship with coyotes and deeply appreciate the chorus that they will set up in the wild mountains. To me they represent the Old West, not the wilderness, but wild land and cow country. The presence, even though unseen, of bears, bobcats and mountain lions adds an essential flavor to the outdoors. I wish we had not killed off the wolves from the country I know best. Coyotes try, but they do not have the same affinity with the remote and truly wild as their larger cousins.

A taste for wilderness probably cannot be acquired late in life as one might develop a taste for martinis or wine, unless there is some predisposition toward it. The percentage of people who really care for wilderness must always be small, along with those who care for great art or vintage wine. It can be increased by education of the young, but probably cannot be indefinitely extended. This is fortunate, since there is not enough great art, vintage wine or wilderness to go around and none of it can be mass produced.

There are those who feel acutely unhappy away from the hum of the central city. Even the suburbs seem depressingly quiet and uninhabited to them. There are the thoroughly extroverted, "other-directed" people who only come alive in the presence of others and fear that if left completely alone they will cease to exist. These could appreciate wilderness if they experienced it with a large group in some mass excursion. Of course, in such a group they would not experience wilderness at all, only wild scenery as a backdrop for social interaction. In a seminar held by Resources for the Future, J. B. Jackson stated that the modern view of wild nature is that it provides a variety of settings for social intercourse, and that appreciation for nature itself has largely disappeared. This viewpoint frightens me when I think about it very long, but I cannot really accept it. I believe that there are very many who appreciate nature as long as it is not too raw. The rural landscape and the quiet country lane are for them. The wooded stream bank near the road, the orchards and fields, rocks and hedgerows of a thoroughly humanized land have the greatest appeal. They like birds and trees and flowers and the lesser or more gentle mammals. Renewal of contact with country ways restores them and they prefer to have a village inn await them at the end of a day's excursion. Wilderness may be important to them, but only as natural beauty. True wilderness experience would not be desired and might even be feared.

For those who have the taste there are fortunately some truly wild places left in the world. These may not always meet the test of the wilderness purist. The vegetation may be disturbed and there may be old traces of man, but they are wilder than most formal wilderness areas. I have seen some of them, but not enough. I recall an evening spent on a kopje near Fort Tuli in Rhodesia. All around was debris left behind by the pioneer column of 1890 and some by later visitors. The vegetation was battered by past misuse of fire and the passage of too many

As long as the impala graze nearby you can feel secure.

livestock, but the land was as wild as one could want it to be. Feeling apprehensive about lions, and wondering where the elephants would be that night, I still thoroughly enjoyed the sight of seven big kudu bulls trooping by, one at a time, from one patch of scrub to another—each brightly marked in its new summer coat, all bearing massive, twisted horns. And then there were the impala, who shared my apprehension. I felt secure as long as they grazed peacefully nearby.

In North America there is not much really wild country available until you head north toward the Arctic or south into the tropics. Even there it is not enough, since man has a pervasive influence. Even a small settlement in the Arctic has an appalling radius of destruction around it. Churchill, on Hudson Bay, is the end of the line for the railroad and is reached by no highway. Its two thousand people occupy a small strip along the shore, but their junk and debris, their trails, fires and the effects of their hunting have modified an area that I would estimate at four hundred square miles within which no landscape is really wild. In the Arctic in particular a feeling of irresponsibility about polluting the landscape seems prevalent. Perhaps because people are so few, and the land is covered by snow for so much of the year, no one hesitates to throw his garbage anywhere. It

Churchill on Hudson Bay, the center of a large area of disturbed and littered countryside.

may well be that the sight of an old beer bottle gives some a sense of human occupancy and well-being in these great wild stretches.

Any vegetation map of North America shows a wide belt of green stretching from Alaska eastward around the lower edge of Hudson Bay and on across Quebec to Labrador and Newfoundland. This is the boreal forest or taiga that extends from the hardwoods of the northern United States up to the very limits of tree growth where the dwarf shrubs and herbs of the tundra take over the Arctic landscape. But if one flies north across it, beyond Lake Winnipeg and Manitoba toward Hudson Bay, or over Newfoundland and Labrador, he will wonder why it is called forest at all, since most of it seems to be covered with water. This is a land of lakes, interspersed with outcroppings of glacier-scoured Laurentian-shield granite, the oldest rocks on the continent and the anchoring post for the North American

The taiga. A land of lakes and dark spruce forest.

Outcroppings of glacier-scoured Laurentian shield granite.

land mass. Lakes alternate with bogs, and only a moderate percentage of the land is occupied by upland forests of white spruce. More of the vegetation seems to be of the moisture-adapted black spruce and tamarack and the lower heaths and sedges of the bogs. The white lichens that grow beneath the trees and provide food for the remaining woodland caribou are visible even from high in the air. Why these lands have remained largely trackless is apparent when the difficulties of road construction are considered. It is far easier to go by boat and portage across the narrow necks of land.

Yet even in this discouraging terrain the lure of mineral wealth has brought increasing human settlement. Mining has brought the railroads north to Thompson and Lynn Lake in Manitoba. From these a network of roads and disturbance spreads out into the surrounding wild country. A highway has pushed north to The Pas and Flin Flon in western Manitoba and the lure of good fishing brings the tourists north each summer. In Saskatchewan roads go even farther north to Otter Lake and Churchill Lake. In Alberta still farther to Yellowknife and Rae on Great Slave Lake. In the historic Yukon where the call of gold once brought hordes of prospectors on foot across Whitehorse Pass and north to Dawson City, the roads now go farther, north to Chapman Lake and soon all the way to Fort McPherson on the far Mackenzie River. In Alaska, Point Barrow, the farthest northern point of the mainland, is now a thriving center for scientists and military people, even though it has yet to be reached by either rail or highway. The plane has largely taken the place of transportation by road, rail or sea in the Arctic, and brings men to all of the far corners: to Thule in Greenland and Alert in Ellesmere Island far north on the Arctic Sea. Still the Arctic remains basically wild. Winter dominates man and landscape alike.

The polar regions are just not like anyplace else. The very timing of day and night by which all men of more settled lands set great store vanishes here. In a world where there is no sunset in summer and no sunrise in winter all other values are shaken. One feels as remote from the temperate landscape as a dweller on another planet. At midnight when the sun is low and the sled dogs are barking or howling, the perception dawns on a

Tundra. No ordinary country for ordinary men.

visitor that this is no ordinary country for ordinary men. Where the fringe of forest dwindles and the mosquito-guarded tundra takes over, one can look north forever and feel that between him and the pole and beyond to the edges of the Soviet land, over thousands of miles, there is likely to be no other human being.

The Arctic would be barren and lonely were it not for wildlife. But the tundras are the breeding grounds for hundreds of thousands of ducks and geese, shorebirds and a variety of upland species. They are the homes of the once mysterious lemming, whose numbers climb to great peaks so that the land swarms with them and then dwindle over a single season to an almost invisible level of abundance. Studies of their aberrant behavior at high levels of abundance, when actions necessary to their own survival are abandoned, may cast light on our own behavior in our metropolitan swarms. Within the forest the snow-shoe hare follows its slower cycle of peaks and crashes in abundance, and out in the tundra the white Arctic hare may add comedy to the landscape with its wild scamperings. But the dominant animals of the tundra, the true bearers of the spirit of the Arctic wild, the wolf, the polar bear, the musk-ox and the caribou, have been gravely threatened by man's activities.

The giant white bear of the polar region, equally at home on land or pack ice, once went its lonely way little disturbed by Eskimo or the occasional white hunter or trader. The airplane changed this picture and removed security for the bear. Now a hunter could leave his New York office on a Friday evening and spend Sunday flying low along the Alaskan coast searching out some unsuspecting bear who had hoped to return home after a hard day's pursuit of harp seals on the pack ice. Some hours later the bear could be converted to raw material for a rug. Steady pressure from such trophy hunters, from Eskimos armed with rifles, from the ever-growing numbers of people who come to the Arctic on government service or other pursuits, has led to a decline in the numbers of polar bears.

The polar bear is not adapted to be preyed upon by other species. Except for man he has no real enemies in all the Arctic. The bears have no tricks of behavior that will protect them from hunters and no high reproductive ability that will allow them to recover quickly from losses. In 1965 an international

The Arctic habitat. Lichens and dwarf shrubs, grasses and herbs.

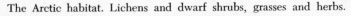

conference was held to consider the worldwide danger to the survival of the polar bear. The Russian delegation focused attention on the urgency of the problem by asking for a world ban on polar bear hunting. The ban needed the agreement only of the five polar powers—Canada, the Soviet Union, Denmark, Norway and the United States. The American delegation, however, was unable to approve so stringent a restriction and the measure did not pass. The northern bears remain in danger.

The key predator in the Arctic is not the bear but the wolf. Feeding as it does primarily on caribou, the wolf has for thousands of years helped to maintain the balance between these grazing animals and the vegetation of the tundra and taiga on which they depend. Although quite capable of bringing down the largest and healthiest caribou bull, the wolves have been shown to prey most heavily on the weak and sick caribou, the stragglers from the herd. Thus they not only remove the surplus from herds that might otherwise overgraze the fragile lichen ranges, they also help maintain the caribou herds in a healthier state than might otherwise prevail. Now, however, the caribou have been thrown out of balance by man's activities. Fires have spread over the upland Arctic ranges, killing out the slow-growing lichens and reducing the area available for the support of caribou. Hunting by Eskimos, Indians and others has been allowed to take a greater toll than the caribou could tolerate. Caribou numbers in Canada dwindled from millions down to a few hundred thousand.

To protect the caribou, man's efforts have been directed not so much at the control of hunting, but at the politically more popular elimination of the wolf. Predator control specialists have gone to work over the Arctic with planes and poison. Over great stretches of tundra now the howl of a wolf has become a sound from the past. Without wolves the land cannot be the same— some reason for its existence will have gone. The tundra food chains that lead from the shallow layers of soil above the permafrost through cotton grass, dwarf birch and reindeer moss to lemming, hare or caribou to their final link in the wolf or its smaller kindred predators are being shortened. The adaptations to an Arctic climate that have developed over ten thousand years

Caribou. Without wildlife the Arctic would be barren and lonely. (*Photograph courtesy of National Park Service*)

or more are being undone. The world is being made safer for man and those animals voted to be popular with people.

Far from the Arctic lands activities are carried out by man in the name of Peace and Freedom, for the glory of France, the People's Republics or the United States. The mushroom clouds from nuclear blasts have pushed upward through the sky from the deserts of Sinkiang or the far Tuamotus, and have spread their lethal components in the global currents that circulate far above the surface of the ground. In the cold Arctic the currents descend and the Arctic soils become fertilized with elements that were previously unknown—radioisotopes of strontium, cesium and iodine among them. Were it not that living things have qualities not known to the inanimate world, these lethal chemicals might slowly disintegrate and do little harm. But plants concentrate elements needed for their metabolism to a far greater degree than these occur in the soil, and have no ability to discriminate between such an element as calcium and its counterpart radio-strontium. Lichens pick up more fallout elements than most other plants, perhaps because they bypass the soil to a degree and absorb materials deposited upon them from the air. Caribou, feeding at times exclusively upon lichens, build up a still greater concentration of these radioisotopes, and with them the danger level is exceeded. Fallout that may be considered at a safe level in the atmosphere or the soil thus increases to a less safe level in lichens and may reach an unsafe level in caribou. Should an Eskimo in turn fill up on caribou meat he will set the Geiger counters clicking far too fast for his own security. Nowhere else on earth does this effect seem so severe, but then in few other places on earth are food chains so simple and the numbers of species of plants and animals so few as in the Arctic. The earth's wildest lands seem destined to gather the evil fruits of civilization's most insane endeavors.

But barring the ultimate consequences of man's misuse of atomic energy, all Arctic stories are not tales of failure. The Canadian Wildlife Service has restored the once-depleted herds of musk-oxen. These strange Arctic cattle were brought to a critically low level by the continued attrition caused by human hunting. With protection and some attention to their habitat requirements the musk-oxen now appear to be safely abundant once again. Farther south, Canada has also preserved the bison, both the wood buffalo and its plains relative, in the 17,300 square mile wilderness area of Wood Buffalo National Park. Here the buffalo herds roam with a freedom little changed from that enjoyed before man appeared on the American scene.

In Canada and Alaska one of the most spectacular areas of wilderness is not in the flat taiga or tundra, but in the mountains that extend from Alberta and Mackenzie westward to the coast of the Pacific and the Bering Sea. The names of these mountains are magic to those who know the ways of the north: the Brooks and Alaska Ranges, the Selwyns and Stikines, the Selkirks and the Cariboos. These are northern extensions of the Pacific coastal and Rocky Mountain ranges of the United States and reach their acme in Alaska where Mount McKinley towers 20,320

Mount McKinley towers above the wild country of its national park. (*Photograph courtesy of National Park Service*)

feet above the wild country of its national park. They reach their most unstable section in the volcanic Aleutian Range where Mount Katmai in 1912 staged one of the most spectacular volcanic eruptions in history.

I have flown over the mountains of Alaska and was impressed with their grandeur. In Canada I have spent more time. The total mass of mountain scenery with one range following on another gives the feeling of an endless wilderness. The mountain heights are not so great as in the higher Rockies or the Sierra of the United States, but the height above timberline is greater and the area of permanent snowfield and glacier is larger. The total effect is not equalled south of the border.

Canada still possesses much that the United States has lost. Its western mountains support a variety of larger wild mammals that is unequalled in the western hemisphere. In Banff and Jasper National Parks mountain goats and mountain sheep are common animals that all may see. Any tourist on the Trans-

Canada highway may have his fill of moose watching. Coyotes, elk, mule deer and black bear are campground hangers-on. One gets so used to them that they scarcely bear comment. The mountain caribou, related to the barren-ground form of the taiga and tundra, still roams the undisturbed forests and alpine meadows in the northern areas of these parks. White-tailed deer, lynx, mountain lion, grizzly bear and wolf complete the list of larger mammals. Among the smaller, but unusual species, one can hope to see wolverine, fisher, red fox, marten, mink and otter. Admittedly the usual tourist does not encounter grizzlies, wolves, caribou or mountain lions, but wilderness starts not far from the

Canada's Rockies—the feeling of an endless wilderness.

highway, and unlike most United States wilderness, it still has its full complement of animal life.

By United States standards, Canada has done well by the wild country of its western mountains. The national parks in the high mountains of British Columbia and Alberta include more than five million acres of land, more than two and a half times the size of Yellowstone. These provinces also have a system of large provincial parks. Tweedsmuir, the farthest north and equal in size to Yellowstone, Wilderness Park adjoining Jasper National Park on the north, Wells Gray, Bowron Lake, Garibaldi, Manning, and Stratchoma Provincial Parks together make a remarkable series of largely roadless, mostly undisturbed, and thoroughly admirable areas. In all of them a great variety of larger wild animals may be found. For the wilderness fancier the absence of major roads in most of the country is reassuring, although to the Canadian progress booster it may be deplorable. Outside the parks are areas several hundred miles across that are not yet crossed by any highways. To a refugee from megalopolis this can be strangely comforting.

If a trip into the wilds of Canada or Alaska is enough to raise the spirits of those who love wild country, the reverse effect is obtained by a journey south of the Rio Grande. Here there should be plentiful wild country since the population is not excessively dense and much of the country is rough and difficult to tame. But shifting agriculture and exploitative grazing can wear out land quickly, and Latin America has suffered from both for a long time.

Aldo Leopold wrote an essay of unusual charm in his "Song of the Gavilan," about a stream in the Sierra Madre Occidental, near the border that separates Chihuahua from Sonora. The river was wild when he visited it, and dropped from mountains where wolves still howled on the rimrocks among the pines. Not long before, the grizzly was still there, but it had been hunted out by 1937 when Aldo and his son Starker Leopold visited the region. Still the land was remote even if the prospects for the future were not hopeful. Leopold wrote: "One of the facts hewn to by science is that every river needs more people, and all people need more inventions, and hence more science; the good life depends on the indefinite extension of this chain of logic. That the good life on any river may likewise depend on the perception of its music, and the preservation of some music to perceive, is a form of doubt not yet entertained by science.

"Science has not yet arrived on the Gavilan, so the otter plays tag in its pools and riffles and chases the fat rainbows from under its mossy banks, with never a thought for the flood that one day will scour the bank into the Pacific, or for the sportsman who will one day dispute his title to the trout. Like the scientists, he has no doubts about his own design for living. He assumes that for him the Gavilan will sing forever."

But it was not science that came to the Gavilan, but destructive exploitation. In 1948 when Starker Leopold revisited the area, and again in 1952, he found it forever changed and wrote of it in a requiem entitled *Adios, Gavilan*. There had been timber there, not much, but enough to attract the loggers. When the loggers built roads it was easier for the stockmen and the hunters

When even the coyotes are gone there is no longer much hope for the mountain. (*Photograph courtesy of Thane Riney*)

to get in and out. By 1952 "one could drive throughout the basin on logging roads, and much of the country was severely grazed. From our campfire we heard much musical yapping by coyotes and not one of the deep, stirring howls of the wolf, although we saw a few wolf tracks." Now the Gavilan and its wolves are a memory of a wild stream on a wild mountain. Progress rolls on. Starker Leopold wrote: "The Gavilan can offer little to the 'good life.' It will produce some beef and some lumber and then probably be left stripped and gutted to its basaltic core. Might it not have yielded more the way it was? Must there be a cow on *every* hill, a road in *every* valley?"

The coyote adapts. So long as wolves are numerous, coyotes are scarce. But man and livestock and wolves do not thrive on the same mountain. Coyotes take over as the last howl fades away. When even the coyotes are gone there is no longer much hope for the mountain.

Perhaps even more interesting than the Gavilan is an area called the Sierra del Nido, north of Chihuahua City. Here an unusually rough terrain had kept people out, even though one could look from the summit of the mountains down on the major highway that ran south from El Paso. Surviving, at least until recently, in these mountains were a few of Mexico's last grizzly bears and the only grizzlies between there and Wyoming, far to the north. Here they carried on in their old wild ways along with the cougars, black bear, coyotes and the ever-present deer. Their home will probably not be disturbed by logging, but their presence is known and it is difficult to keep hunters out. Most recently I have heard that they are being killed by 1080 poison, a contribution of American science, spread out by one of the ranch owners in the area. There are many people who do not like big bears. They seem to challenge man's right to destroy all land, everywhere. They defend diversity.

If we use grizzlies and wolves as indicators of the remaining true wilderness in temperate Mexico, then the Sierra Madre Occidental as far as the great *barrancas*, equal in grandeur to the Grand Canyon, is one of the remaining areas. Along with it is the grizzly country north of Chihuahua City and some of the lands on the border between Chihuahua and Coahuila. The Sierra del Carmen that adjoins the Big Bend National Park in Texas also qualifies on the basis of cougars and bighorn, and should be part of an international park. A population of wolves has been reported by W. W. Dalquest from the wild western portion of San Luis Potosí, well to the south. But that was in 1953 and much has since happened.

Since the settlement of Mexico brought people crowding into the temperate highlands one might hope that the tropical low-

Big Bend National Park. The Chisos Mountains. (*Photograph courtesy of National Park Service*)

The rain forests of tropical America represent a last area of wilderness.

Logging opens the way.

The charcoal gatherers follow the loggers.

lands were more nearly intact. To a degree this is true. The map will show a roadless area that extends from Yucatán through the Petén region of Guatemala and around through Chiapas to southern Vera Cruz. But the impression of wilderness is misleading. Most of the people in this area do not require highways and their works do not appear on maps. They are Indians or subsistence peasants who will still follow the old tropical land-use practice of slash-and-burn. This has destroyed more tropical forest than anyone not familiar with the tropics would be willing to believe.

Where roads are built peasants move in.

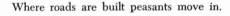

Parks and reserves may exist on maps and signs, but signs don't stop settlers.

A crop of taro where once was forest, then erosion and abandonment.

The slash-and-burn or *milpa* system is believed by some to have eroded away the lands on which the old Mayan empire depended and to have been responsible for its collapse. The descendants of the Mayan in Yucatán, where old temples still rise from the forests, have used the *milpa* system to remove virtually all of the older forest and cause its replacement by second growth and scrub. The system involves clearing of a patch of forest with the subsequent burning of the forest debris. Crops are planted in the opening until the fertility of the fragile soil is depleted and yields decline. The planters then move on to clear a new patch and the old is allowed to grow back into forest. At least this is how the system used to work. Today clearing is often followed by planting until the soil is more thoroughly exhausted or eroded than in earlier times. When the area can no longer be farmed it may be turned over to grazing. Eventually the grass loses out to scrub, but any hope of rain forest recovery within a human time scale is quite remote. The land is ruined. The older system did little damage, but it was adapted to a sparse population and there was adequate time for forest recovery. Now that population pressure on the land is severe the consequences are often little short of disastrous. Although basically a tropical system, the *milpa* has been widely employed in temperate areas of Latin America.

Starker Leopold has described an area in the hills north of the Valley of Mexico, described as beautiful pine-oak forest by Alexander von Humboldt early in the nineteenth century, that is now completely barren, with the soil entirely eroded. This is extreme, but other areas representing various stages in land destruction are more common.

In the tropics the logger often leads the way in the assault on the rain forest. The timber cutters move in to get mahogany or other high-value woods. To get machinery in and logs out, they build roads. These open the way for the *carbon* gatherers who come in next, converting the wood that remains into charcoal for use as fuel in the towns and villages. Next the subsistence farmers move in on the cleared ground and the cycle of destruction is well under way. Destruction of tropical forests in Mexico goes on at a rapid pace. Most of the forests of Vera Cruz have been seriously affected, extensive clearing has gone on in Chiapas and pressures are developing in Tabasco and Campeche.

If the wolf and grizzly are indicators of true wilderness in temperate America, the jaguar, curassow and great tinamou are indicators of undisturbed, climax conditions in the tropics. The jaguar does not require climax forest. This great cat, known as *el tigre* to the *latinos*, is highly adaptable and much inclined to wander. It is not, however, compatible with man, and is unwilling to take up civilized ways. It is poorly behaved around people. Starker Leopold has described it well: "Around the camp fires of Mexico there is no animal more talked about, more romanticized and glamorized than *el tigre*. The chesty roar of a jaguar in the night causes men to edge toward the blaze and draw serapes tighter. It silences the yapping dogs and starts the tethered horses milling. In announcing its mere presence in the blackness of the night, the jaguar puts the animate world on edge. For this very reason it is the most interesting and exciting of all the wild animals of Mexico." Where jaguars are abundant, wilderness still prevails. Leopold has found two such areas: one centered in the rain forests of northern Chiapas and Campeche, the other in the still undisturbed dry tropical forests on the west coast of Sinaloa and Nayarit.

The curassow is a large member of the fowl family, a bird the size of a turkey, black in color with a lumpy casque on its yellow bill and a feathered crest resembling some hair styles common on our college campuses. It is a bird of the tall rain forest that does not thrive elsewhere. When the rain forest is logged it disappears. With the jaguar it has a center of survival in the wilderness of Chiapas and Campeche which it shares also with a similar, turkey-sized bird, of less exacting habitat needs, the crested guan.

The great tinamou is a strange bird belonging to a family more closely related to the ostriches than to other living groups. It is, however, a flying bird, the size of a chicken, dark in color to match the darkness of its rain forest home. Along with the curassow, the crested guan and the jaguar it finds a home in the Chiapas-Campeche-Petén wilderness. This area supports other animals that tolerate little interference. Among them is the big tapir, a relative of the rhinoceros and the horse and the only member of this order to survive as a wild animal in the Americas. Over much of Latin America it has been killed out and now survives only in remote rain forest. Where you find tapirs you may also see the belligerent white-lipped peccary, a relative of the pig, that roams in herds beneath the forest canopy.

There is little effective wilderness preservation in tropical America. The idea that there should be a place on earth for the remote and wild, for the undisturbed forest and its peculiar animal denizens, has not penetrated to the average citizen nor to most government officials. There may be laws on the books and reserves marked on maps, but protection ends there. The land is seldom patrolled, the laws are rarely enforced. It is argued that governments that must concern themselves with poor and illiterate people have more important things to worry about than nature. People cannot appreciate amenities until they have necessities. This truth is obvious, but it accentuates the dilemma. There are necessary priorities for action and some things cannot be postponed. It will take no food from anyone's mouth to protect the better areas of the wilder lands. There will be no chance to do it later, when other supposedly more pressing problems are solved. The people may some day be fed, but the environment that could have enriched their lives will have gone.

My emphasis has thus far been on Mexico since it is the best known and in many ways the most advanced of the Latin lands of North America. Next to the United States and Canada it is the wealthiest country on the continent. If conservation efforts do not succeed here they will not be won elsewhere in tropical North America. Farther south there is still wild country in existence, but the speed at which it is vanishing is rapid. Costa Rica, the wealthiest and most literate of the Central American lands, has an appalling growth rate that approaches 5 per cent increase in population per year. There are still some wild lands in the southern part of Guanacaste province and east of the cordillera near the borders of Nicaragua and Panama. But the *milpa* and other land-use practices take their toll. Here are some disturbing examples of forest clearing, rapid degradation of cleared lands and scouring erosion carrying topsoil out to sea.

The visitor may be told that Costa Rica has a system of forest reserves, but these are almost meaningless. Peasants settle everywhere and destruction moves with them.

Only a program of technical assistance and perhaps financial aid from other nations is likely to save the remote wild resources of the American tropics. But such aid and technical assistance as we give seems geared to economic development and to acceleration of the processes of destruction. There are many first-rate biologists in Latin America. There are many who see the need for saving the lands and their resources. But they fight an almost irresistible tide of human increase. It does not seem that they can win.

The wilderness of the American Arctic and the tropics is far more precious to all of us than most of us can possibly realize today. It represents a last chance to save not just unchanged vegetation on sample areas, but a complete biota, including species that have been eliminated within the temperate United States and Canada. It is wilderness in which the sense of danger can still live, wilderness where man can face up to the raw, elemental side of nature if he so desires, and thus restore some sense of contact with his own evolution, his long ancestry in the wilder reaches of the earth. It is wilderness that shelters the great beasts that cannot coexist with civilization, and protects those fragile or timid creatures that also need a world that man has not disturbed.

7

Where People Live

The air has got a scum on, an' it takes yer breath away:
The sun ter save yer life you wouldn't know—
                                    —Montague Grover

WHEN we worry about the environment, we are worrying about man. The wind could howl endlessly over the world's deserts, the sun could shine forever on the luxuriance of a tropical rain forest, but what would it matter if mankind had gone? We can leave vast areas alone, but it is only worthwhile if those areas are of significance to someone, somewhere. For a billion years before man appeared on earth, nature experimented with life and threw its failures away. Only man weeps over the fallen.

We cannot generate any pressure of concern over the wildness of the world, over the faraway islands or remote tribes of people, unless we pay attention to the majority of mankind. More and more this majority is city born and city oriented. Unless we reach them, we fail. You cannot talk of nature to somebody who has seen it only in a city dump, whose unconscious dreams are framed in concrete and steel, pollution and ugliness. Unless we build understanding and sympathy into the minds and hearts of the city dweller, we will fail in our efforts to preserve a diversified, vital environment. When the millions in Calcutta cry out to preserve the wild Himalayas, when Harlem votes to preserve the grizzly bear, the battle for the human environment will be won. Until then the fate of our own species will also be in the balance.

In the capital of our nation where the great plans for the future are drawn and uplifting words about the improvement of the American environment are spoken, we have allowed urban distintegration and moral decay to become prevalent. Those who should have been responsible, and who may have spoken or written the noble words, have too often fled to the distant countryside, or have isolated themselves within the few enclaves of beauty and order that persist. But a few blocks from the White House is a skid-row atmosphere where striptease palaces vie with penny arcades, where bookstalls feature pornography and movie theaters cater to those who like to see sex mixed with sadism. This is the edge of an area of hopelessness and dirt, disintegrating neighborhoods and helpless people, where the streets at night are safe for nobody.

Not far from the White House—an area of hopelessness and crime begins.

In the wilds of Michigan where Antoine Cadillac once founded a fort, the city of Detroit has grown, dedicated to the production of vehicles that bear his name and to their rivals and lesser counterparts. The "large and beautiful rivers that replenish all the lakes" of which Cadillac wrote are now drains for sewage and the wastes of the factories pouring into a dirty and dying Lake Erie. One would not think you could kill a great lake, but we are managing it. The influence of Detroit is felt far afield, wherever the products of its industry are concentrated in great numbers. Everywhere the battle of the freeway is being fought in an effort to prevent the destruction of cities by the automobile and its adjuncts. In Los Angeles, despite some heroic efforts, and in New York, with no effort at all, the menace of automobile-borne air pollution grows, demanding new solutions if we are to continue to breathe.

Why we have allowed such problems to develop cannot be understood without reference to our history and attitudes. Whether the steps we are taking to correct them are sufficient is

The influence of Detroit is felt everywhere. Washington ranks high in air pollution, largely a product of motor vehicle exhausts. (*Photograph courtesy of U. S. Public Health Service*)

debatable. Many have pointed out that the cities of America are the new frontier where the "great society" must be formed. They are the place where attitudes toward all America will be conditioned. One wonders what attitudes toward the American land are formed in the schools of Harlem and Watts or the slums of Washington.

The confusion of our cities today reflects our past attitudes, our unwillingess to plan far enough ahead, our inability to control the activities of our own citizenry to an extent necessary for their own good. Today, however, our cities receive more care and attention than ever before. Those who forget the past should review the scenes of fifty years ago described by such writers as Barbara Tuchman or Frederick Lewis Allen, or earlier by Upton Sinclair and Lincoln Steffens. Our water is polluted today, but rarely deadly. Our air is smog-filled, but we do not have to breathe the fumes from the "satanic mills" of the last century. In those earlier days there was little protest since protest was of no avail. We have fought in the past fifty years an enormous revolution to achieve for the common man some basic rights, and this revolution has largely been won. The socialist of yesterday demanded less than the capitalist of today gives without question. Yet the fires kindled by this revolution still light dreams that we still destroy and hopes that we cannot satisfy. Yesterday's problems were severe, but localized. One could get away from polluted environments. Today's problems are growing universal and daily more severe.

The confusion of our cities reflects past attitudes, an unwillingness to plan, an inability to control the activities of our citizenry.

Our cities rarely grew by plan but mostly by circumstance. Every old district reflects a thousand individual decisions that in some places created charming neighborhoods and in others confusion and distress. Only a century ago did the cities face up to the responsibility of providing some police and fire protection to their citizens. Only in the past few decades have they assumed responsibility for the public welfare in any comprehensive sense. City planning was once confined to the monumental designing of capital; today few cities lack their planning staffs. The haphazard methods of the past led to many little mistakes, but gave not too much room for big ones, and did produce some unique and interesting places. The centralized authority of today makes mostly big decisions, for good or bad. There is the danger. The cities of the year 2000 do not just exist on drawing boards, they are already taking shape around us. We must live for a long while with the mistakes that we make today, and we may be making big ones.

I have heard Rene Dubos point out that we know far more about the wild animals for whom we build homes in our zoos than we know about the human animal for whom we are now building cities. The need for further research on the biology of man is acute, particularly his ecology and his behavior. There is an enormous diversity still existing among people and it is worth preserving. It will be unfortunate if our architects and planners build a million rabbit hutches and then find that wolves and foxes must live in them.

My own concern for cities is deeply mixed with my interest in wild nature. When I was thirteen years old I started my career as an amateur ornithologist in a big city. The impetus was provided by books I had read about the fascination of natural history, and some childhood experience in wild lands. Since I could not study bears or mountain lions in a San Francisco flat, I started with the available wildlife, city birds. The first four supposed species that I carefully described in my notebook and then sought to identify in the manuals all proved to be different sex or molt phases of the English sparrow. After this ignoble beginning I added a domestic pigeon and an unidentified sea gull to my "life list." The area in which I lived at that time was later to be listed for urban renewal, and I may well have been underprivileged, although I did not know it. The neighborhood, however, was not too attractive for birds. I recall a great day when the first truly wild bird, a hermit thrush, took up residence in the garden next door.

Bird study was a secret vice that I kept concealed from the members of my school peer group, known at that time as a gang. I had won with great difficulty, through use of unarmed combat, a position of some respect in this group, and did not wish to jeopardize it by appearing to indulge in suspect, intellectual pursuits. Consequently I used to sneak off before or after school hours to search out birds in their haunts. The nearest possible haunt was one called Alta Square, a park that encompassed four square blocks on top of Fillmore hill. It ran mostly to lawns and Monterey cypress and seemed to attract few more birds than the neighborhood yards. The other possible bird area nearby was the City Hall plaza, some ten blocks away. This, however, was mostly carefully pruned plane trees, black wattle, concrete and ornamental fountains. It was a good gull ground at times, but mostly ran to pigeons.

I was to find my principal source of birds and information in Golden Gate Park. Here I discovered that the California Academy of Sciences had public exhibits of all the common species. It also yielded for a small sum a guidebook to the local birds that took the place of the eastern manuals that had previously been available to me. My education began in earnest in this more distant environment, a half hour walk away. Here I struggled to distinguish the Nuttall from the Gambel white-crowned sparrow, and went on from there to add some scores of species to my list of known birds. Here too I became acquainted with the ways of brush rabbits and fox squirrels, and even encountered tracks of skunks and raccoons.

I spent many days in Golden Gate Park without mishap and without ever thinking it was a dangerous place. I remember a few suspicious and threatening-looking characters that I left behind by some fast footwork and a knowledge of thickets and trails. Mostly, however, the park was serene and inhabited by families, tennis players, hikers, horseback riders, and no doubt,

Golden Gate

Presidio

Richmond District

Golden Gate Park

Buena Vista Park

Rocky Hill

Mission Park

Sunset District

× Mt. Sutro

★ Twin Peaks

Sand Dunes

Zoo

× Mt. Davidson

Lake
Merced

San Bruno Hills

SAN FRANCISCO
THE FORMER OPEN SPACES

other bird watchers. It was a park, however, that varied considerably. The east end, near the diversified homes, rentals, shops and cafés of the Haight-Ashbury district, was always well inhabited by birds and people and was friendly. The west end, in the single-family suburban area of Richmond and Sunset, was rarely visited and had few birds. In part this was because of the physical arrangement and vegetation of the park, but the distribution of people also reflected the life of the surrounding neighborhoods.

The neighborhood in which I lived was not a beautiful area but it was diversified and interesting, and thoroughly urban. It could not have existed in a small town or suburb. However, I lived not just in a neighborhood but in the city, to a degree that I think few cities are lived in now. I roamed from the cliffs of

the Golden Gate to the hills of San Bruno. I watched ships
land on the bay and waded in icy waters off Ocean Beach. For
my family the city was a home and we knew all parts of it—the
area in which we happened to have a house was not the center
for social life—San Francisco was.

During my bird-watching days I was to learn all of the open
spaces in San Francisco and to rate them as spaces for birds.
The eucalyptus groves around Mount Sutro were gloomy, monot-
onous areas that supported few birds and attracted few visitors.
The grasslands and scrub that extended from Twin Peaks to
Mount Davidson was wild country where one could forget the
existence of the surrounding city. It was a land of meadowlarks
and sparrows, rabbits and hawks, that attracted packs of boys
and dogs. The sand dunes that then occupied much of the Sunset district were highly attractive as playing space for children,
and although their bird life was limited, they provided a good
substitute for the Sahara Desert for someone with imagination.
Rocky Hill was also not much for birding, but provided cliff
faces in the old quarry that substituted for the high Sierra as
rock-climbing surfaces. This area also supported an extremely
rough neighborhood gang who were the equivalent of a hostile
tribe of Indians and added to the adventure of trespassing in
their territory. I distinctly recall one time when they were shoot-
ing at my cousin and me with a twenty-two rifle, and we were
retaliating by rolling large boulders down on them. There were
no casualties, but I think we would have qualified as juvenile
delinquents by modern classification. I know they would.

As I recall, most of San Francisco's parks, with the exception of
the eastern half of Golden Gate Park, Mission Park, the downtown squares and areas that offered special attractions such as
the section around Fleischacker Zoo, were little used. One of
the larger and more scenic, Buena Vista Park, a heavily wooded
hilltop, was usually empty. I did not hear any of them being
described as dangerous, as they are now, but they were not
popular. Also, most supported few birds, since uniform stands
of black wattle, ti-tree, eucalyptus and other exotic trees seemed
to attract few native species, and green lawns are popular with
only a few kinds of birds. By contrast the varied cover of tree-

lined streets and private gardens in Berkeley, across the bay, supported a surprising number and variety of wild birds. These childhood observations and later experience lead me to believe that if we construct parks that people really want to visit, they will also be places attractive to wild birds and the smaller wild mammals. If we construct cities that are really fit for people, diversified cities that people can identify with as I identified with San Francisco, then those cities will also be inhabited by squirrels and rabbits, wild birds of all kinds—generally the more fastidious wildlife with habitat requirements more exacting than those of man. If we build cities that are concrete deserts or inhabited only by rats and starlings, we will make a home only for rat-like people and colonial-roosting people of the kind who foul their environment.

A great surge of urban renewal is under way across America. Cities are being taken apart, and sometimes are put back together again. New cities, suburbs and towns are being constructed to make way for the ever-growing numbers of city dwellers. But what kinds of places are we building?

In 1966 I attended a planning meeting in Philadelphia, a city that has taken the lead in recent years both in urban design and city planning, and in the implementation of the designs and plans. I had read such encouraging accounts of the progress of Philadelphia that I was looking forward to my first visit to this planning Mecca rising in the East. I believe that I went with an open mind and a willingness to accept the new ideas that were being implemented in this most historic city.

My first tour at this meeting took me to Penn Center, the heart of downtown where the statue of William Penn towers on its city hall pedestal above the tops of the skyscrapers. Here blocks of the old city had been and were being demolished. I am told it was an ugly old place. To replace what was old, new high-rise office buildings, hotels and apartment buildings have been constructed, separated from each other by open malls and roadways. Each new structure was a gleaming monument to twentieth-century functional architecture—clean and devoid of artifact or artifice—straight towers of stone or concrete or metal, in cross-section rectangular, square, circular or arc-shaped. Un-

fortunately, my eyes kept straying to the nineteenth-century complex ornateness of the city hall, the medieval citadel of the
Masonic temple and the spire of the central Methodist church.

Penn Center is not all on the surface, however. To make room
for automobiles, pedestrians are being routed underground. Beneath the streets will run another series of malls, opening here
and there to the light and air through garden courts. Here will
be located various shops and services. Still lower are the central
stations of the mass-transit systems, bus, railway and subway
stations. Space in the city center is thus used efficiently and
ameliorated by as much beauty as the architects and designers
can manage.

After spending an hour or more examining the wonders of this
new city center I felt depressed—by the absence of people and
of life except for trees, shrubs and flowers growing in greater or
lesser concrete pots. I moved to what was left of old Philadelphia,
into the narrow streets, the dirty old converted town houses, the
jumble of shops and theaters and the mixtures of older tall
buildings. Here, and not in the new malls, was where the people
were—crowding the sidewalks, moving into theaters or pubs,
traveling to or from church, window-shopping. I ate lunch in the
back of an old delicatessen and worried about the future.

I worry about being fair to something that has taken so much
thought and effort. I saw Penn Center on a Sunday, which could
explain its emptiness. Also, it was not completed and the shops
and features that might attract people had not moved in. The
sunken ice-skating rink did have both skaters and watchers, while
some people were eating in the restaurants. I returned once
more on a Monday. There were more people, but still the disturbing contrast between the bustle of the old streets and the
sterility of the new. I went on down the parkway toward Logan
Circle and admired the public buildings and the sweeping view
toward the art museum. There were not many people there either.

Philadelphia is a striking city with a central core of skyscrapers building up to a peak at Penn statue; with its clear
definition between the tall canyon streets of the city core and
the lower levels of residential and mixed-purpose structures that
surround this center; with its sharp central city boundaries set

In our urban renewal we sometimes take the life out of our cities. Outside the new shiny towers there is no place to go, nothing is happening. (*Photograph above courtesy of Department of Housing and Urban Development*)

Everywhere we are tearing our cities apart and rebuilding them, creating great monuments to our architectural skill and sense of urban design. Constitution Plaza, Hartford. (*Photograph courtesy of Department of Housing and Urban Development*)

by the rivers on two sides. Beyond the rivers there is sprawl, and near them is ugliness from neglected fields and marshes and a jumble of oil refineries, docks and industrial structures of all kinds. Yet the central city has a quality that overrides the surrounding ugliness.

Here are some of America's most historic buildings, once obscured I am told by a surrounding confusion of none-too-pleasant housing. Now the surrounds are being cleared and the glories of Independence Hall, Carpenter's Hall, the First and Second Banks of the United States and other monuments to our past are exposed in public parks and a new, flower-and-tree-bordered mall that provides both public open space and a sweeping vista.

Independence Hall was swarming with Sunday visitors and its immediate square and adjacent mall were well occupied. But as I wandered past the banks toward the Custom House to admire the towers designed by I. M. Pei down by the river, I was almost alone in this urban open space. I knew there were people in Mr. Pei's towers, since I could see their cars, but they did not come out. Only at Bookbinder's old restaurant near the river-front were there people once more. I walked back through some beautifully designed park spaces that lead from Independence Square over to Washington Square. Trees and shrubs, paved spaces and brick walls were artfully placed. There were three or four people there, sitting. Washington Square had more life, squirrels, pigeons and a few dozen people. Back over in Ritten-house Square where old, new and reconditioned town houses mix with apartments, hotels, offices, shops and restaurants, people were numerous. The square was fully stocked with sitters, walkers and sprawlers.

It is good for a nation to have monuments that tell of past glories and present abilities. Monumental cities need parks and plazas to set off their architectural glories, to provide views and contrasts to mix the charm of living things with the grandeur of the buildings. Paris is a monumental city that all the world admires. But I saw it first in winter when all the people were crowded into the cafés and bookshops of the Left Bank and the grand boulevards and parks were windswept and empty. I wondered what Paris would be like in winter without the crowded little streets where the people were. In our urban restructuring in America we run a risk of creating great dead monuments to our engineering skill and forcing people either to accept a sterile, if well-grassed, environment or to leave the city that we are trying to revitalize. We need pay more attention to the diversity of those areas toward which city people gravitate.

I have not been reassured by a visit to Pittsburgh. From high in the Hilton Hotel I looked down at the junction of the Allegheny and Monongahela Rivers that form the "golden triangle" of downtown. I wondered how a city could afford to let its freeways dominate its open space to such a degree. The tall, new, shiny towers of office and hotel stand isolated in their malls and parkways. Fortunately a friend showed me the way out of the empty malls over to the old, crowded area of red brick and turmoil where people pushed their way around the sidewalk fruit stands to cram into hole-in-the-wall bars and restaurants. Here I wondered again if we were rebuilding our cities for real people, or just to satisfy some yearning in the souls of architects and engineers.

I have written much of this in Georgetown, which visitors to Washington know as the place "where the action is." Most Georgetonians wish that the action could be moved somewhere else, since visitors and tourist-oriented action are killing George-

Georgetown—row houses that are here called town houses; old gardens and tree-lined streets.

town. Georgetown has no impressive monuments, and the open space within it is largely confined to private gardens. But these are old gardens from which cherry trees, magnolias, wistaria and forsythia may shower blossoms in the wind; and the streets are lined with tall trees where cardinals, mockingbirds, blue jays and squirrels abound. There are some fine old houses that have been graced by the occupancy of many from America's Establishment. There are other not so fine places that are of the same vintage and design as slum dwellings elsewhere in Washington, row houses that are here called town houses to suggest that the owner has also a country estate; three and four story buildings that have been arranged into many apartments. But the houses are polished and cherished, restored and modernized. Rents are exorbitant and real estate prices unbelievable. On weekends everybody seems to be in Georgetown, causing one huge traffic jam and filling the sidewalks. The quaint specialty shops do an enormous business selling at inflated prices items that can often be bought elsewhere for less.

Georgetown has vitality, diversity and a beauty enhanced by the parks that surround it on most of three sides. Only its waterfront is ugly, and that will be changed. But it is hardly an urban ideal. From the time that I arrived I was warned against walking around at night on its residential streets. Whether or not they are safe I do not know, but people do not use them at night. Only in the areas of shops, restaurants and entertainment places are there crowds in the streets. The attractions of night life draw many strangers including a great number of the beatnik variety who are distressing to the older residents. The Georgetown public schools do not educate the Georgetown children, who go mostly to private schools. Consequently, morning, noon and after-school hours see a movement of children and teenagers to and from the often deteriorating districts beyond the borders, and these show little respect for the amenities of Georgetown life. The area is too much an enclave of the wealthy and the unencumbered young adult in a big city world of urban distress. It needs a better mix to survive, and it needs the creation of many more equally attractive and magnetic centers of urban life beyond its borders.

One Sunday in March 1966, I first went with my family on a pilgrimage to Reston to see one of the widely publicized new towns in what will be a new city located southeast of Washington in Virginia. Reston represents a concept in community planning that has been gaining a wide following in the area to be encompassed by the great megalopolis of eastern America. In Reston a deliberate effort has been made to preserve open space and natural beauty within what is expected to be a basically urban region. In this effort the developer, R. E. Simon, has done remarkably well so far. The area preserves the woodland and glade aspect that characterizes the rolling hills of the eastern piedmont. The natural interspersion has been enhanced by the creation of artificial lakes that add a land-water edge to both woodland and glade and provide opportunity for boating and water sports to the Reston people.

Reston preserves open space by use of the cluster-development scheme that is now widely accepted. At one end of the lake is a village center with shops, restaurants and a cultural center grouped together. Above these are apartments, adjoining them rows of town houses, and among these one high-rise tower of apartments. Beyond the town houses are the more usual

Reston—the cluster development approach to new town planning. (*Photographs by William A. Graham, courtesy of Reston*)

suburban detached dwellings on individual lots. These, however, are limited in area and not allowed to sprawl across the countryside. The area is thus intended to accommodate people from several economic levels and with different tastes in housing.

Reston had a holiday atmosphere when we first saw it, and we suspected that this is typical of the Lake Anne Village, the first of its new communities and one inhabited by the true believers, the Reston "pioneers." These people had been captured by the imaginative scope of the scheme and were willing to put up with the inconveniences of development including the absence of schools and community facilities. In time it is hoped that they will live in a largely self-contained city with its own businesses and industries.

Among the strong features of the Lake Anne Village is the "human scale" intended to minimize the use of automobiles by locating all of the daily necessities of life within easy walking distance from the main housing cluster. Walking is encouraged by building attractive walkways and foot bridges across the waterways of the lake. Accessibility for vehicles is restricted. Thus Reston is one of the best efforts of the modern planner and developer. It follows a basic plan similar to that recommended by Victor Gruen in his book *The Heart of Our Cities*. It will have

The need for a different kind of country is sometimes obvious. Washington's Southwest, before and after urban renewal. (*Photograph above courtesy of Department of Housing and Urban Development*)

many features in common with the new city of Columbia, being built by James Rouse and his associates between the cities of Baltimore and Washington.

The cluster development is the widely accepted answer to suburban sprawl and we can expect to see it all across America. It should appeal to the conservationist with its emphasis on maintaining open space. I have tried hard to become enthusiastic about it, since it seems desirable from a land-use viewpoint. The cluster creates a more attractive landscape, preserves natural values, minimizes the use of motor cars and is adaptable to mass transit systems. But when I think of living in one of them, I retreat. My gregarious instincts are normally strained to the utmost by the social contacts of a working day and of organized social events. To me home must be a refuge from social stress. The cluster development with its emphasis on communalism, surrounded by public open space, seems to offer scant refuge.

For several years I lived in a suburb of the kind portrayed in such books as *The Split-Level Trap* or *The Lonely Crowd*. The redwood and stucco house stood on a slope from which the last trace of soil had been scoured by the bulldozers of the builders. In the back lot the barren subsoil contrasted with the virtually indestructible debris left behind when the original redwood forest was destroyed by the developer. All efforts to civilize this barren land seemed futile at a time when my pocketbook would not allow the hauling of soil or the pouring of fertilizer. Even the most hardy plants withered and died. Our picture window looked across the street into the picture window of another house where the "homemaker" attempted to duplicate a *Better Homes and Gardens* scene and lived the open, friendly American way of life. Our side doors opened on one side almost into a neighbor's kitchen and on the other gave access, almost, to a neighbor's garage.

In this house I learned in time to loathe my fellow man. In retrospect I know that my fellow suburbanites were as good a lot as any, and that the way of life for all of us may have contributed to their defeat also. Although they seemed far more friendly and outgoing than I, there was one suicide and two who skirted close to nervous breakdowns, and yet another who shattered the neighborhood calm by pretending to shoot himself with a double-barreled shotgun. It was not a happy place. The younger children roamed in an upper-middle-class rat pack across the lawns and over the streets. Here my youngest daughter learned the use of stick and brick in defense against little friends with mayhem in their souls. My dog became paranoic. I don't want to go back.

In retrospect I know the tract in which I lived was not the best. I know also that many who lived in it found it more than satisfying. I am contributing my bit to the anti-suburban literature, but as Herbert Gans has pointed out, the picture I am helping to perpetuate is partly false. It is composed largely by displaced "cosmopolites" who should not have moved to the suburbs in the first place. In his words: "it should be noted that the problems of both the cosmopolites and the working-class people result from being in a numerical minority, rather than from suburban residence. They do not suffer from pressures to conform, but from a shortage of like-minded people in their surroundings. Were they to live in communities with more compatible people, many of their problems would disappear." This may well be true. However, when I think of bringing together all of my best friends into a common suburb, I shudder. Under such close and continuous contact we would surely drive each other mad.

Despite the deterioration of our cities there has been always a hard core of urbanites who refuse to live in any other environment. These hang on in urban enclaves of the rich, in mixed city environments where all classes mingle or in the anonymity of large apartment buildings. The city, with its tolerance toward the stranger and its recognition of the necessary namelessness of its hundreds of thousands of residents, provides a degree of privacy lacking in the detached-house suburb and necessarily absent from the suburban cluster. A big city can offer a range of activities, a sense of purpose, a feeling of vitality, lacking in other places. It can bring together people with unusual interests or abilities who would not ordinarily have much contact with one another away from the dense city center—groups of artists or writers, researchers or musicians, food faddists or religious cultists, people from less common cultural or ethnic backgrounds. To the confirmed urbanite the crowded confusion of the city street adds a zest to living. High-density, high-variety cities, completely distinct from suburb or countryside, are a necessary habitat, a necessary part of America's diversity. Enough has been said about them. The urbanite already knows, the non-urbanite will never accept these values.

Traditionally, America has not favored cities and the outlook of most Americans has been rural. Perhaps the majority of past city dwellers regarded their urban sojourn as an unpleasant necessity. Their hearts were in the country and when circumstances permitted they fled to the suburbs. I do not believe that the suburban flight was caused by urban disorganization so much as by rural orientation. Those who fled the city sought space and air and private gardens, along with neighbors who had similar means and wants. If this is true it may be difficult to lure these people back into the city, regardless of how much charm is offered in new town houses and apartments, or the degree to which city organization is improved. Urban renewal programs aimed at luring the middle-class back to the city from the suburbs may fail, as William Alonson has pointed out, if it is not modern housing but private space that attracted them outward in the first place.

There is also a danger that the new towns with their village clusters will meet resistance from the same group. The cluster development may force a degree of social interaction that even a confirmed "organization man" finds undesirable. If people were all happy, gregarious extroverts who did creative things in packs; dominants in the peck order who had amiable squabbles but no real fights; amicable persons who had friendly but never adulterous intent toward a neighbor, the common ground and clustered houses would be assured of success. But there is a potential danger in a clustered village in open space that the ever-present social climate will oppress, that children will skulk indoors rather than face the neighborhood bullies in the common playground. The sociology of the cluster badly needs study before we commit ourselves to it as thoroughly as we have recently committed ourselves to the sprawling suburbs. Once that is done we leave little alternative for the home-buyer with "no down payment."

8

Into the Urban Wilderness

Can one say that where trees cannot live, then man should not try? Can one say that when the most abundant inhabitants, with man, are pigeons, starlings, and rats, a threshold has been crossed and either evacuation or redevelopment is necessary? . . . Where does the canary expire, the litmus change color? where is the disgenic zone, the area of apathetic survival, the environment of full health—and what are the indicators?

—Ian L. McHarg

New York may already be dead. We have no way of knowing.

—Edward T. Hall

AT A MEETING at Airlie House in 1965, Kenneth Boulding, one of those rare economists who understands ecology, had this to say: "You think of ecology as something that is a study of nature in the absence of man, and this is nonsense. The ecology of the aspidistra is just as interesting as the ecology of the whooping crane. The ecology of Harlem is just as interesting as the ecology of Yellowstone Park. In fact, much more interesting, more complex. The ecology of the suburb is much more interesting than the ecology of the wilderness. Who studies the ecology of the suburb? It is absolutely fascinating.

"Yet ecologists have this absurd point of view that all they are interested in is the countryside. I have nothing against the countryside. In fact, I am in favor of people loving it. That is fine. But you ought to love the city, too, and especially the suburb, because this is where people are going to live. This is just as interesting."

This particular meeting is a landmark to me since it took me out of the redwood forests and placed me in megalopolis, where I was supposed to concern myself with the ecology of the city. Unfortunately for Mr. Boulding's statement, Harlem is not an ecosystem, nor is Manhattan. It is more like a termite mound, dependent entirely upon the outside for its subsistence. In other respects, however, I agree with Mr. Boulding, and have been attempting ever since to apply some ecological knowledge to the study of cities. Unfortunately, I keep coming up with the old academic answer to all questions: "More research is needed."

Ecology can offer much to the study of cities but its application will probably not be known under the name of ecology. Systems analysis is after all a recent, computerized counterpart of an old ecological technique of ecosystem analysis, and it has become highly popular among those who study cities. Proxemics, the study of space relationships, of which Edward T. Hall is an outstanding exponent, is an application of ecology to the human scene. Ecologists have long concerned themselves with the space relationships of plants and animals. Ethology, the new science of animal behavior, has as its parents the older sciences of ecology and psychology, and has much to offer to those who study cities. Yet, while there is a need for ecologists in the city, I think most ecologists should stay out in the wilder lands. There are many willing to study the cities, but few willing to take on the study of the endangered wild country. Better that those who study man should have some ecological training, than that those who study wild animals should abandon their efforts. Wilderness and cities are tied together. The answer to some human problem may come from the study of the gorilla in the Congo forest.

Back somewhere toward the beginnings of human time, attitudes were conditioned toward that shelter that is known as home. Passed down over the ages from place to place and culture to culture, these attitudes have varied, but only within limits. I know of no people completely devoid of an attachment to a home space. To some the home territory is a broad one, and the shelter may be carried on the back or constructed from materials available at the campsite, but there remains the concept of a home area to which the individual and his group belong. Completely free-ranging nomads are as rare among people as among other mammals. It is difficult to extend the concept of territoriality, as it exists among birds and some mammals, to the human species. A territory, in the usual meaning of the term, is an area maintained for the exclusive use of the individual or his family group. It may be defended against other individuals of the same species, or it may simply be mutually respected. In strongly territorial species this form of behavior leads to spacing of individuals and groups, and prevents overcrowding. Man is only weakly territorial in this sense, yet the tendency to maintain a home space, from which individuals not belonging to the family group are generally excluded, is common to most human cultures if not to all. Man's territorial behavior does not prevent his overcrowding, but the breakdown of an individual's territory through overcrowding can lead to symptoms of psychological distress, and at times to physical breakdown.

Robert Ardrey in *The Territorial Imperative* has applied the concept of territoriality to human behavior about as far as any one can carry it at this time. Application of the territorial attitude to the land claimed by the clan, the tribe or the nation, and a consequent willingness to rally to its defense against the intrusion of any outsider, is an obvious human attribute that gives unending problems to the United Nations. I have been fascinated also by Ardrey's triangle of amity-enmity and hazard. Amity, the relationship within a homogeneous group, varies with the degree of enmity, opposition from outside groups, and hazard, environmental forces other than those generated within the species. When hazard is high, enmity is low, and all groups cooperate to survive against a common danger: fire, flood, hurricane, volcano or earthquake. When hazard is low, enmity against outside groups must be high in order to preserve amity within the group: e.g., all forget their differences when war is declared against a common enemy and the degree of amity increases as the enemy becomes more threatening. Finally, however, if there is neither external hazard or enmity, amity falls to a low level and all intra-group differences are magnified. Unfortunately, despite Vietnam, this is the situation in which we find ourselves today, and it is reflected most strongly in our cities.

"The house is a refuge [where people] can regroup their energies for interaction with that outside world."

In a study of human behavior in relation to housing in public projects, Lee Rainwater has this to say about human attitudes: "Because the house is a refuge from noxious elements in the outside world, it serves people as a locale where they can regroup their energies for interaction with that outside world. There is in our culture a long history of the development of the house as a place of safety from both non-human and human threats, a history which culminates in guaranteeing the house, a man's castle, against unreasonable search and seizure. The house becomes a place of maximum exercise of individual autonomy, minimum conformity to the formal and complex rules of public demeanor. The house acquires a sacred character from its complex intertwining with the self and from the symbolic character it has as a representation of the family." When this character of a house is violated, when it no longer serves as a refuge, those who dwell in it will suffer consequences worse than those to be found in many so-called slums where the houses may be wretched, but are at least safe and private.

The feelings toward a house extend outward to the surrounding grounds. To the degree that these act as extensions in breadth of the walls of the house, the house will seem that much more secure. The security can be enhanced by the presence of congenial and friendly neighbors. It can be offered also by extending the privacy of the house through the exclusiveness of private open land. Open space that offers no such feeling of security can in some circumstances be useless. Therein lies the cause of difficulties encountered in some kinds of public housing that have seemed attractive on paper, but have proved only to reinforce feelings of insecurity.

A desire for private land is not so universal as the desire for a private home and many live in apparent contentment in city apartments with no land of their own. Even those who care deeply for their own plot of ground would hardly vote for having all land private. I have lived in areas where this was too much true, and remember the feeling of relief on reaching a bit of common ground where I felt my rights to be as great as those of any other citizen. The common ground, whether in city park or national forest, is as much a part of the western tradition as the private plot.

Many live in apparent contentment with no outside ground of their own. (*Photograph below courtesy of Department of Housing and Urban Development*)

The quality of living in our metropolitan areas may well depend on the amount and kind of open space that is available.

The quality of living in our great metropolitan areas may well depend on the amount and kind of open space that is available, and if all kinds of people are to be accommodated, on the proper balance between public and private open space. From my own childhood it was inevitable that I would be an advocate of open space in and near the cities, where children could learn an interest in nature and where wild things could be made available to those who lack the time or money to journey far from home. Yet it is also apparent that urban open space can be misused to disrupt a city, to break apart the centers of vitality that have kept the city alive and to aggravate feelings of insecurity.

Our current attitudes toward open space in the cities are tied rather tightly to our attitudes toward urban density and over-crowding, basically our attitudes toward space relationships. Because overcrowding of people was admitted to be bad, through experience gained during the dark period of the industrial revolution, we have used various devices to prevent it. Density zoning, limiting the number of residential units per acre of land, has been one technique used against it. At one time such density zoning

Density zoning prevented crowding and congestion, encouraged the development of space for living within the city.

was beneficial, since it prevented the crowding of units together, unbearable congestion and the breakdown of city services. At a later time these same density limits have forced suburban sprawl far out into the countryside, have increased the difficulties of providing necessary services, including efficient transportation, and have made it difficult to create or maintain an urban environment.

Working in Honolulu, Robert C. Schmitt examined the question of density and overcrowding in relation to health and social disorganization. Density, the number of people per unit of area, was distinguished from overcrowding, the number of people per unit of housing. By holding overcrowding as a constant in his study, Schmitt was able to show a clear relationship between density and such indications of social disorganization as illegitimate births, juvenile delinquency, crime and various levels of physical and mental ill-health. Dense populations in Honolulu appeared to be less healthy and more subject to social breakdown than sparse populations. Overcrowding, where not accompanied by high density, did not appear to have the same effects.

On the subject of density relations among mammals other than man, ecology has much information to offer, and yet raises more questions than it answers. John Calhoun has received the most attention among social scientists and city planners for his studies on density relationships among rats. He has contributed such terms as the "behavioral sink" and "pathological togetherness" to the literature. Calhoun has shown that when laboratory rats are released into a common area, even though it provides abundant food, shelter and water, their populations do not increase above a level that is much lower than those that could be maintained in the same space under laboratory conditions. At this level, there is every evidence of social disorganization and physical breakdown. Crowded rats show evidence of sexual and

We have yet to establish a clear relationship between high urban densities and social disorganization.

social pathology that is distressingly reminiscent of that which occurs in a city slum. One is tempted to find a direct relationship between density, the number of rats per unit of area, and psycho-social pathology. But one must remember that one can crowd much greater numbers of rats into a much smaller area without evidence of physical or psychological breakdown, if one provides each with his own cage, brings food and water to him and removes his waste products.

If we are going to consider rodents, however, we had better look at other experiments, particularly those of F. Steiniger on brown rats as reviewed by Konrad Lorenz and those of Charles Southwick, working with the white-footed mouse, and I. Eibl-Eibesfeldt, who worked with the house mouse. These showed that the species in question could tolerate high densities so long as the animals with whom they associated were known animals, either relatives or animals that carried the familiar smell of the cage and the clan. In Lorenz's words: "In their behavior toward members of their own community, the animals here to be described are models of social virtue; but they change into horrible brutes as soon as they encounter members of any other society of their own species. Communities of this type possess too many individual animals for these to know each other personally, and in most cases membership of a certain society is identifiable by a definite smell, common to all members." Regardless of density, the strange rat or mouse introduced to these colonies is set upon and is killed, or dies as a consequence of the constant harassment.

Studies of other mammals can only suggest directions we might take in the study of human ecology—they do not provide direct answers to human questions. We do not know, for example, to what extent high urban density is undesirable, since Schmitt's studies in Honolulu and other studies of which I have heard do not clearly distinguish between density as such, social organization in the sense of the relatedness of the members of the community—the degree to which they know and trust one another—and physical organization, the ease with which people can obtain the necessary goods and services. All of these interact.

Anyone who lives in a large American city is familiar with the frustrations that come with high urban densities. Traffic is

Before we rule out high urban density as such we should consider other factors—the physical and social organization of communities among them. Few planners would want to eliminate such districts as Montmartre simply because of high density.

jammed, air is polluted, water is unfit for use. Everywhere one encounters masses of people attempting to do the same thing at the same time. One waits in lines at the grocery, the theater, the garage. Often it is faster to walk than to drive or use public transportation. At lower densities, out in the suburbs, many of these frustrations are removed. It is tempting to draw the cor-

People are not alike. We need to build diversity into our cities if we are to accommodate human variety.

relation between distress and high density and to seek solutions
to city problems by liberal applications of open space and by
limits on density. But should the relationship prove to be not
one of density but of the physical organization of private and
public space or the social organization of the inhabitants, then
the new cities—both the high-rise in park-like surroundings, and
the town-house clusters in new village complexes—may well have
built into their common grounds all necessary conditions for
future social distress. If we are going to spend vast amounts of
money on building housing for the human animal, is it not time
we spent more money on studying the kind of creature we are
accommodating?

I do not wish to overstress criticism of this or that way of
solving the problem of living in an urban environment, but only
to indicate that people are not all alike and that much more
study is needed. I have a persistent worry that someday America
will become blandly uniform. This has been reinforced by my
moving to the eastern coast where the natural scenery is much
the same from one place to another. In the West man's efforts
are ameliorated by the stark contrast of mountains, deserts, rocky
shores and diversified vegetation. In the East it is more necessary
that man provide the contrasts, that he seek to build into the
new cities and strengthen in the old the maximum degree of
diversity in cityscape and townscape. By such means he can
also provide the different kinds of ecological niches that different
kinds of people require. But the government must take an active
part in sponsoring urban diversity. The private builder risks too
much whenever he attempts to introduce anything entirely new
or even attempts to re-create something that is obviously old.

It is generally agreed among city planners that the proper use
of open space is essential to sound urban design, to the creation
of viable city communities and to any attempt to give to the
city a distinct and recognizable image that its citizens can comprehend and appreciate. Parks, playgrounds, natural areas, outdoor cultural centers, all of the varieties of public open space
are an integral part of a well-organized city. Yet today the future
of such open space is in danger, from high land values and the
consequent demand to use all open space for building, and

The proper use of open space is needed to give the city a recognizable image. London's Hyde Park.

particularly from the motor vehicle and the tendency to invade all open areas with freeways or parking lots.

When areas of conflict develop between those who favor construction and those who favor preservation, there is often an opportunity to resolve the difficulties in some alternative approach that will satisfy both sides. The exception to this process seems to be the conflict between the highway builder on one side and those who favor open space and beautiful cities on the other. The conservationist develops the feeling that the engineer is equipped with mental blinders that enable him to think only along narrow tracks, unaware of ideas on either side. The engineer must feel that he is encountering sentimental irrationality that does not fit either slide rule or computer. I get the feeling sometimes that if a method of route analysis used by highway planners indicated that the least expensive route between two points in Washington led through the middle of the Capitol building, the highwaymen would advocate that route, and congressmen would be found who would defend the choice, arguing the advisability of separating Democrats from Republicans with a freeway.

Undoubtedly, one of the greatest dangers to the American city and landscape today lies in the unholy alliance between engineers and automobile manufacturers. The automobile has replaced the deity as an object of worship for mid-twentieth-century Americans. Whatever sacrifices it demands seem to be forthcoming. Despite my knowledge of the problems that too many motor cars present, I find myself reading the car ads and wondering whether I should buy a cool, foreign sports car, or some high-horsepowered Detroit production. I fight the extensions of freeways in the wrong places, but feel a great sense of relief when I leave a crowded avenue and spin onto the beltway. I know there is a fairly reliable bus at the corner, but I drive to work and pay dearly for parking. The national schizophrenia surrounding the freeway-automobile problem is internally familiar to me.

Perhaps the most outstanding example of the clash between the highwaymen and the city has been presented by Sam Zisman, a Texas city planner who has been in the thick of the fight. San Antonio, Texas, has or had a remarkable open space system of the kind that seemed to work. Its various components were fully appreciated by the public. They included such things as picnic grounds, a zoo, a golf course, an Audubon bird sanctuary, a natural area and nature trail, a wooded river course, a Girl Scout camp, a college campus, various public school grounds, an outdoor theater, and so on. Through, or in some way disrupting, all of these the proposed North Expressway would run. Efforts to prevent this met with complete resistance from the highwaymen. Open space was to them space for a highway. As Zisman has commented:

"It has been observed in other places, in other cases of expressway controversies, the fight has centered on the despoliation of a park, *or* the disruption of a neighborhood, *or* the severing of a campus, *or* the bisecting of a zoo, *or* the loss of treasured trees and landmarks, *or* some other single loss—but in the case of the North Expressway, practically all are involved in one great wholesale invasion." The unfortunate thing is that, at the time of Zisman's writing, the invasion seemed irresistible. Urban open space appeals to highway builders because it usually can be acquired with less cost and conflict than privately owned, built-over land. However, if we are not to throw out any effort at achieving a properly designed, integrated city environment, we must maintain the open ground, the parks and walkways and natural areas, along with the built-up land. Zisman has suggested an approach to the problem that is more realistic than that in use today, stating that "open space is not the left-over land, or the vacant land, the unused land or the waste land. It is of an equal order of consideration with any kind of development. . . . open space is in the design and planning sense the 'fixed' element, the building areas the 'free.'" Unfortunately, his approach has yet to win enough adherents to give the protection that the cities need.

The disrupting effect of the highway on the city has been dwelt upon at great length by Lewis Mumford, Victor Gruen and many others, and I will not belabor it here. The highway will not go away nor are Americans likely to give up automobiles until forced to. The problem of accommodating the automobile is largely a problem of planning and design of the city itself. Rarely is an answer to an increase in motor vehicles to be found in the addition of more freeways.

There are times when I feel that the combined effect of the automobile and the television set has already killed our old city centers—that "downtown" is dead and cannot again be revived. This feeling is reenforced when I visit the barren wastes of downtown Washington at night, or wander through the area that still goes by the name of Broadway and Times Square in New York, but no longer has any of the old spirit. The need of people to congregate for entertainment, the pleasure that was gained from rubbing shoulders with the crowd during an evening out, may be found today only among those who have not yet joined Marshall McLuhan's world village of television. All others now stay home in their suburban cages and feel one with the world as portrayed on the picture tube. The only ray of hope that I see for downtown is that today's college generation, raised on television, have fled away from it, and are finding their own urban centers in which to congregate. One may not approve of the types that one encounters on Berkeley's Telegraph Avenue, Washington's M Street or in New York's Greenwich Village, but at least they are participating and represent a still surviving area of life in otherwise largely deserted downtown regions.

The disrupting effect of the automobile on the city, the decline and decay of the central city and the ever-growing extent of air and water pollution are receiving much attention today in virtually every book written or speech delivered on the subject of the urban environment. However, these are only various aspects of a much more serious problem that still receives inadequate attention—the problem of urban growth.

Urban growth and its accompanying urban sprawl have combined to produce the metropolitan or megalopolitan aggregations of people in areas that are now no longer cities nor countryside. Such areas continue to grow at disturbing rates, rates that seem to be defeating the efforts of planners, designers, city councils and county supervisors to contain, control or direct the process in any rational way. In metropolitan Washington, for example, there are dozens of excellent city plans, but growth is so rapid that sprawl and disorganization outrun the efforts of government to keep up with it or make it conform to a plan. In looking forward to the future, the governments of metropolitan regions, of states and of the nation seem to be concerned only with the problem of accommodating population growth and somehow managing to keep their planning a few steps ahead of the pressure of increased population. Only a few seem to be considering a different approach, that of containing and controlling growth.

In an earlier book on California I noted that the continued growth of the Los Angeles metropolitan area and of other southern California areas represented a problem to the entire state. To accommodate these growing numbers it is necessary to mortgage the future, disrupt the natural environment and destroy values in large areas throughout California. Yet planning for California has been based on the assumption that these ecologically misplaced populations must be allowed to grow, and in fact that their growth must be encouraged and subsidized by statewide efforts.

Writing about the problems of Los Angeles, Allan Temko has made this statement: "There is room enough in the Super-City not for 20 but for 30 or 40 millions of people, if only we have the wisdom to conserve the resources which remain unspoiled, and to renew the resources which have been wantonly damaged. We must decide where we should build, and where the wisest course would be to leave land undeveloped, according to the full scope of future needs." Whereas I agree in general with Mr. Temko, his attitude toward population growth is ecologically absurd and colors his otherwise excellent ideas about the future development of Los Angeles. The same misguided hopefulness is found in statements by most political leaders in all parts of the nation. All attempt to evade the full issue of population growth.

The regional plan and various general plans for southern California assume that population growth will continue, that ten million people will become twenty million in twenty years and that we must plan to accommodate them. However, if the plans are successful, and nobody assumes any responsibility to control growth, the population must inevitably continue to grow. Plans must then be made for Allan Temko's forty million in southern California, and to the extent that these are successful, growth will take place to fulfill the plan. And so we go on to eighty million and beyond with the planners making brave statements and seeking to accommodate to what they believe to be the political realities of life. However, such projections soon become absurd since the natural resources to support such continued growth are not available: the air is not available, the water is not available, the food will not be available, and most of the amenities have already disappeared. On probing more deeply into the thoughts of those who speak only of accommodating growth through good planning, I find a belief and hope that some day, without any effort on their part to encourage the process, people will slow down their rates of reproduction, migration or both. I cannot determine the source of faith that kindles this hope.

The growth in Los Angeles, or in any other metropolitan area, is caused by two factors: birth rates that exceed death rates, and immigration rates that exceed emigration rates. Decline or stability depend on lower birth rates, increased emigration rates, decreased immigration rates or, although we hope not, on increased death rates. Leaving aside for the present the question of birth control, growth in an urban area can be controlled by increasing the outward movement of people and discouraging inward movement. Both possibilities are within the control of political authorities. The reason why people move to Los Angeles is not obscure nor does it relate too strongly to the supposedly excellent climate. Most people move to Los Angeles because Los Angeles promises more jobs and opportunities for advancement than most other cities offer. The jobs are there because industry, retailing, education and other employing agencies have been encouraged, or have been permitted, to locate there. If these employing agencies were not encouraged, if they were offered incentives to locate elsewhere, they would go elsewhere and population growth would move with them.

The issue of controlling urban growth has been faced in other areas. Grenfell Rudduck, writing of the need for national planning in the redevelopment of Australia, suggests that new cities should be located at points well away from the present metropolitan regions of Adelaide, Melbourne, Sydney or Brisbane, in the far north and in the interior. Not only would these accommodate people who are now clogging the facilities of the existing centers, but they would provide urban facilities and cultural amenities to these now remote, and in some ways backward, areas. To quote from Rudduck's conclusion: "It will be a herculean task to re-orient our city-based economy. No one, to my knowledge, has yet established beyond doubt the economic advantages of planning medium-sized cities of say a quarter to half a million compared with the multi-million mammoths that are now developing. But, in any case, we don't choose to live as cheaply as we can. We have long since passed the bread line. Today people prefer to live as well as they can. What will offer the best life? Where does the choice lie? I know where my choice would be."

Homer Hoyt, writing in *Land Economics*, points out that urban size can be influenced and growth in new places encouraged by federal action alone, through the awarding of defense contracts or other federal incentives to industrial relocation. State governments, however, must contribute their share to the process by location of educational facilities, state institutions and other state services in the selected region. Writing also in *Land Economics*, Joseph Mangiamele discusses the need to

The congested traffic in big cities creates the demand for freeways—but these are often destructive to both the open space and the urban structures that give character to the cities. (*Freeway photograph courtesy of Department of Housing and Urban Development*)

Sydney. Continued growth threatens to destroy the charm of an environment that has thus far enriched the lives of its people.

discourage growth in the existing southern urban centers of Wisconsin, and to encourage it in the more remote centers of the north, such as the existing town of Superior.

William J. Levitt, said to be the nation's largest home builder, in testimony before the Senate Housing Subcommittee in 1966, called for a major federally sponsored program aimed at the building of entirely new cities well away from all existing metropolitan regions. Believing that further accretions on our existing metropolitan regions will aggravate rather than solve our problems, he called for the use of the federal urban development act to provide the capital needed to establish these new urban centers. Such an amount of capital, which he estimated at one billion dollars for each new city of one hundred thousand, is beyond the ability of private industry to provide. It would represent, however, a sound investment for the federal government, since in these cities "future generations may live and work, learn and play, grow up, raise families and enjoy—really enjoy—all the good things and benefits that this wealthiest of nations can so fully provide." Similar ideas were expressed by other builders at a conference on environmental design sponsored by the National Association of Home Builders in Washington in 1965.

To return to the California scene, nobody sensibly suggests that Los Angeles will be improved by further population growth, or that the southern California coastal plain needs more people. Further growth, even with the best of planning, can only come at the expense of those outdoor amenities that have attracted visitors to Los Angeles. Twenty million Angelenos cannot go surfing, nor can they find space in recreation areas of the nearby mountains. Even with smog-control devices that are now on the drawing boards installed on every automobile, twenty million Angelenos cannot continue to drive their cars without poisoning their air beyond all tolerable levels. Even if all of the streams in California and northward are harnessed to meet the needs of Los Angeles it is unlikely that forty million people can be provided with all the water they want or need, assuming that through the massive state water plan under construction the needs of twenty million can be met. If it were absolutely necessary to accommodate such growth, a matter of life and death, with no alternative, the monumental efforts needed to do so should be attempted. But it is not necessary. It is not even sensible.

By contrast the isolation and cultural backwardness of California's far north could be cured by the development of northern cities. At present there is no city between San Francisco and Portland, Oregon, a distance of over six hundred miles. But there are attractive sites at such points as Redding and Eureka, sites that have plentiful water and an abundance of space. In earlier times transportation problems inhibited growth in these areas, but these can be solved far more readily than the water and pollution problems of southern California. Bold decisions by state and federal authorities are needed to accomplish such a shift from south to north.

Even more congested than the Los Angeles area is the eastern Boston-Washington conurbation. Efforts are being made to direct growth in this region through metropolitan planning, and to check sprawl by building totally planned communities such as the new towns of Columbia and Reston. Yet all of the new towns fall within the already urbanized region. They are in Levitt's words "encrustations on the swollen megacities that are engulfing us." They compound the confusion already existing in megalopolis, where water sources are already inadequate, streams are dreadfully polluted and transportation is in an enormous snarl. Despite this no serious thought is given to the question of limiting growth. Instead, we are told to plan for four million where two now live and such growth is stimulated by further encouragement of employing agencies. All this occurs in a nation

We need not follow always the same patterns in the same places. It is possible to build places that are different.

where the Rocky Mountain states, the Intermountain region, and the Great Plains continue to lose population or at best hold steady. A rational scheme of national and state planning would bring new and better cities to these areas, even if industry had to be bribed to move there and citizens offered overseas pay to induce them to settle. A new city in Appalachia, for example, might offer a solution to both the excessive growth of megalopolis and to the wretched poverty of that old land. But such a city will not just grow, or it would already be there.

The question of how big a city should be is one for which there is no single or generally acceptable answer. Jacquetta Hawkes has pointed out that small cities can serve just as effectively as cultural and intellectual centers as large ones. Athens, Florence and other centers of Old World learning and culture reached their flowering while still just large towns by modern standards. The giant city, with few exceptions, is a result of the industrial revolution and was not common before the middle of the nineteenth century. But little is to be gained by arguments about the relative values of high versus low urban densities or big versus little cities since the problem of limiting city size does not hinge upon absolute numbers of people but on the quality of the urban environment and the impact of city concentrations upon the total environment.

Our ability to provide efficient transportation, clean water, desirable housing, adequate public and private open space, clean air, food and other supplies necessary to the functioning of a massive, urban agglomeration has been severely tested and has proved inadequate. Our ability to remove the waste products produced by massive concentrations of people and industry has been strained to an even greater degree. We are not doing an adequate job and probably do not yet know how to. Further growth, particularly rapid growth, can only complicate these already unsolved problems.

In such places as Chicago, Detroit and the eastern seaboard cities we have a multi-billion dollar task ahead in just cleaning up the existing pollution of the Mississippi, the Great Lakes, the Potomac, the Hudson and virtually all other surface fresh waters and estuarine waters. This assumes that we can do the job at all, which is by no means certain. The expenditure of even more

billions of dollars to keep fresh water available and avoid pollution for cities that are doubling in size would be wise only if
there were otherwise excellent reasons for concentrating more
people in these areas. We cannot say for certain that a small city
is better than a large one. We can say, however, that our existing
super-cities will be much worse places when their sizes are
doubled. Consequently the enormous efforts being made to
make possible continued growth in these cities are being made
with the knowledge that life will be less pleasant, and perhaps
intolerable, when the efforts are completed. It would surely make
sense to spend the billions elsewhere, in places where the problems would be less perplexing.

There are those who wish to keep all wide open spaces wide
open. These people cheer at the news that the population in the
Rocky Mountain region is decreasing. They would prefer all
people to move to megalopolis and leave the West free for trees,
wild animals and those happy few who prefer a really outdoor
way of life. Some northern Californians prefer to ship their water
to Los Angeles rather than have Los Angeles people move north.
While I sympathize with these feelings I cannot believe that they
represent an answer to even their own problems.

The influence of a city does not stop at the city limits. The
people of both the Arizona desert and the Owens Valley have
found that it does make a difference to them how big Los
Angeles grows, since it grows with water they could have used.
The defenders of wilderness find that a dam builder seeking a
source of city water is an irresistible force, and starting with
Yosemite, our national parks and wilderness areas have been hurt
by his activities. Furthermore the city populations of America
do not stay in cities. Summer sees them swarming from their
urban hives into all the wild places. The wide open spaces seem
neither wide nor open when a hundred million visitors move
in. Instead the open lands are regimented to suit the needs of
the urbanites. The wild country will be kept in better shape if
our people live in humanized, attractive cities from which natural things have not been excluded. A half million people from
a new city located perhaps at Cheyenne, Wyoming, would take
care of Wyoming's wild country better than would a half million
refugees from Greater New York.

9

Refuges for People

I thought, We have geared the machines and locked all
      together into interdependence; we have built the
      great cities; now
There is no escape. We have gathered vast populations
      incapable of free survival, insulated
From the strong earth, each person in himself helpless, on
      all dependent. The circle is closed, and the net
Is being hauled in. . . .

                           —Robinson Jeffers

I HAVE spent some time worrying about what I do not like about modern technology and why I am worried about the future of technological society. There are some objective reasons and some that are highly subjective. There is a dilemma, also, since, like most people, I do not want to give up the benefits of technology.

The substance of my personal objections can best be exemplified by my reactions to commercial air travel. I travel by air frequently and prefer a fast jet to a slow propeller plane. Yet once in the air I am uneasy, and when I land I am tired and disoriented. My reaction is against being transported at a speed I cannot comprehend by a device that is beyond my control. If anything goes wrong, nothing can be done; I have turned my existence over to an electronically controlled mechanical object. Reason and logic do not prevail against this feeling. I feel uneasy, for the same reasons, in the skyscrapers of downtown Manhattan. Here too is an environment beyond my control, crowded by people who similarly lack ability to control their surroundings. A power blackout, a breakdown in any of the systems upon which the metropolis depends, and all are left helpless. New Yorkers who experienced the 1965 power blackout are familiar with this feeling of helplessness and realize that our technology is far from foolproof.

Since I moved to the eastern megalopolis I have a feeling of dissociation from a natural environment that I did not know in California. Even in the crowded circumstances of San Francisco or Los Angeles there is always some natural scenery close at hand: the sea, the bay or the mountains. It is reassuring. In the eastern cities, particularly those that are inland, the nature of the terrain makes one feel surrounded almost completely by the man-made and surrounded always by hordes of people that form part of the thirty-five million dwellers in the Boston-Washington region. Such people depend completely on the continued function of a technology they usually do not comprehend and cannot control.

The consequences of detachment from a natural environment

New York in 1962. The air pollution grows worse, the environment more congested. Here one lives in almost complete detachment from natural things in a technological world over which the individual can exercise no control. (*Photograph courtesy of* The New York Times)

and the helplessness that comes from too complete dependence on mechanical or electronic systems affect people who do not always know that they are being affected. It is reflected in the chaotic nature of much of our recent art, particularly the Underground art. It is reflected in the frantic striving for ever more aberrant forms of sexual activity and the flight into drugs and the rise of magic, mysticism, satanism. Creative minds are seeking in the unconscious realities that once surrounded them in daily life. But the unconscious mind is also influenced by its environment. One whose early images were of neon and concrete, garbage and dirt, noise and confusion will hardly build in his inner mind any refuge against the pressures of today's technology.

Marshall McLuhan has interpreted the effects of media upon society—radio, television, print and the other newer devices. He makes use of the concept of autoamputation developed by the medical researchers Hans Selye and Adolphe Jonas. Our technology and the communications media that it involves are extensions of ourselves. Radar and television are extensions of eyesight, radio and telephone are extensions of our sense of hearing. The entire complex of retail and wholesale groceries, transportation, warehouses and our mechanically organized farms are extensions of the primitive food-gathering mechanisms that employed sight, walking, smell and touch, grasping and plucking, capturing and killing. Air travel or travel by wheel are extensions of our old ability to travel by foot. Once we develop an extension of what was once a physiological process we must "amputate" or isolate the senses normally engaged in the process. We cannot see far enough to perceive the object within radar range. We cease looking and depend on the radar screen. When we travel by car we "amputate" the normal senses of balance, sight, touch, pressure and the like that are involved in the process of walking. If we try to respond to a rapidly moving automobile with the same senses involved in walking, we will make ourselves ill. We respond instead to the vehicle itself, using the senses and mechanisms needed to operate it; we respond to speed of travel by vision alone, relegating to eyesight the information gathering that would have been performed by all of our senses were we on foot. In air travel we abdicate all response to the phenomena of travel itself since even the visual sense becomes irrelevant until we arrive at our destination. We travel physically without using the physiological mechanisms associated with movement.

For such autoamputation, however, we pay a physiological penalty. The body has elaborate mechanisms for dealing with the normal exigencies of a wild mammalian existence. These become frustrated in their operation in a technological society. Our intellect tells us that all is going well, but our endocrine system objects to this conclusion. In a society where our actions have often only a remote connection with their results, where we are at the mercy of individuals we do not see or know, where we depend for survival on devices or instruments we cannot control, we are subject to stress of which we are unaware. My dog goes wild when a sonic boom results from a jet cracking the sound barrier. I tell myself it is only a jet and pretend I do not really mind. But where my cerebral cortex may register green for go, my endocrine system is flashing red for danger.

An honest fear of a consciously recognized danger can lead to a healthy flight reaction. A continued anxiety about a consciously unrecognized danger leaves us in a Kafka-esque world internally, where nothing makes sense. A certain degree of stress is essential to living as Seymour Farber has pointed out in a quotation from E. M. Westcott: "They say a reasonable number of fleas is good fer a dog; keeps him from broodin' over bein' a dog." But we have exceeded the limit. Too much stress causes physiological breakdown. Humans and other animals alike can die from it.

Farber has pointed out: "Conceivably, continued research may provide sufficient insight into the mechanism of stress so that physicians will be able to determine the correct amount of hormone required to treat every disorder.

"Yet how much better, Selye suggests, for man to learn to live in greater harmony—with himself and with the world; to live in accordance with his craving for adventure, for variety, for noble ends."

The dangers of our technology are not only internal and psychological but external. Harrison Brown has long ago pointed this out. If we go on building a civilization whose very functioning is dependent upon extracting power and essential minerals from low-grade raw materials, we are building a technology from which we can never again turn aside. The transition from our present state to this advanced technological state could take place smoothly, in theory, but as Brown has said: "It is a transition that will happen only once during the lifetime of the human species. We are quickly approaching the point, where, if machine civilization should, because of some catastrophe, stop functioning, it will probably never again come into existence." The likelihood of such a catastrophe is only too apparent today. Harrison Brown goes on to say that if such a catastrophe should strike: "the less a given society has been influenced by machine civilization, the greater will be the probability of its survival."

Despite the dangers, we seem determined to go down the headlong path toward encompassing the entire world within our technological network. Admittedly there is no essential evil in our technology itself. It is a tool, but one that by its very nature shapes everything that it touches. As Paul Goodman has pointed out, if we only build a single luxury hotel in an underdeveloped country, and then pay the equivalent of luxury wages, or tips, to its bellboys, we disrupt the entire economy of the area. Since a person performing a relatively useless task in the hotel earns more than the most skilled farmer outside, the reason for continued agricultural effort disappears; the social fabric of the local community is torn, the entire value system is shaken.

It is easy to fall into the trap of thinking that we already live in a technological world and that America is representative of it. It is easy to plan for America as if it existed in isolation from the rest of humanity. Yet we are a small, rich minority in a world of poverty. The benefits of technology flow to few. We live in a world where almost every stage of man's cultural evolution is still represented in one area or another, from primitive food-gatherers and hunters through subsistence farmers, fishermen or herdsmen through to the technological aristocracy. The question for our survival is whether we can get along in this world. If we go our own way, getting fat while others starve, if we involve ourselves with others in a way that arouses their antagonism, we will have difficulty in surviving. We tread a dangerous path, indeed, and it is no real consolation to know that the other technologically advanced countries share our danger.

It is easy to fall into the trap of thinking that we live already in a techno-logical world and that America is representative of it, but over much of the earth life follows older patterns.

It is apparent that whatever the disadvantages of our tech-nological way of life, its advantages in material wealth, ease of living and freedom of choice are sufficient to attract those who do not have them. It is also apparent that we are committed to a program of helping the so-called developing nations. Our foreign aid and technical assistance programs are likely to be part of our budget for a long time to come. But how these programs are used can determine whether there will be cultural variety left in the world or whether we will all have to fit the same technological mold.

Map of New Guinea.

During World War II an Australian friend of mine was in an army detachment that was ambushed on top of the Owen Stanley Mountains—by headhunters. His attackers did not know there was a war on, but they knew strangers and could recog-nize a trophy head. At a time when it was normal to be blown apart by bombs and artillery, it seemed incongruous to have men die through being speared. Today, in our electronic, nuclear-powered world, the headhunters are still there in New Guinea—primitive peoples with odd ideas of adornment, still pursuing their stone age traditions, engaging in inter-tribal raids, carrying on in their old subsistence agricultural ways as though the twentieth century did not exist.

I know that we are required to interfere in India and Puerto Rico, that to prevent mass misery and starvation we must help advance these people on the fringe of technology to a more developed technological life. But there is a question of why we have to do anything at all about New Guinea. For the most part the New Guinea people, if not disturbed, would show no inclination to join us. Admittedly we have disturbed them often. Missionaries, driven by the archaic beliefs that still survive in our society, have gone in to Christianize them. Others, who think that all people everywhere must have modern medical care, have gone in to touch off a population crisis. Some have gone in for perfectly obvious reasons, to get the gold, the pearls, the copra. We have taken many of the Papuans and shaken them out of their old ways, civilized them in a fashion, consoled our consciences by giving them more material goods than they had previously known or wanted. But still most of them were little affected. During World War II the coastal fringes of the island were stirred and in places shattered, but in the interior life went on in its old archaic patterns. Then came the United Nations and the great period of "enlightenment." Colonialism became a dirty word and New Guinea was being primed to take its place in the council chambers of the United Nations. People from many ethnic groups speaking some seven hundred different languages are being forced to take their place as a so-called nation in today's world.

Few would deny a people's right to live in the technological world if they so desire. But must they be forced in? Do we really have something worthwhile to offer that all people, of necessity, must want and have? When the Papuan comes out of his mountains, removes his feathered headdress and the bone ornament from his nose, will he really be better off living in the Papuan equivalent of a Lima *barrio* or a Brazilian *favela*? After all it is the menial work of the technological world that will be available for most of these people. They will not all become college graduates, speak in Parliament or fly jet airplanes. Should we really insist that they join us? If we do, is it for their own good, or just because we want to sell them automobiles and buy their mineral ores?

Primitive communities are easily disrupted. I have been told that when cheap metal axes were first introduced to the Australian aborigine the entire structure of tribal society was disrupted. Previously axes were of stone, hard to come by and a symbol of male power and authority. But every woman could have a steel ax, better by far than the old stone ones. Perhaps the aborigines were better off with the status of women improved —I have not heard the end of the story. The balance between a primitive culture and its environment is easily disturbed. A single new tool can shatter a relationship between man, soil and climate that sustained a people over thousands of years. The knowledge of when to plant, what to plant, how to hunt and find water, what is edible and what is poisonous, passed down by oral tradition over centuries can be lost quickly. With the total package of information passed from the tribal elders, the society can prosper. If a few parts are lost, or thrown out of balance by some innovation, the entire framework can disintegrate.

The Kalahari Bushmen lived for centuries in an environment where we cannot survive without an uninterrupted flow of supplies from the outside world. But they wilt and die in contact with another culture. In Rhodesia our houseboy was telling us, one day, about life in his home village, describing his cattle and possessions. "Who takes care of these while you work in the city?" my wife asked. "My Bushmen do," he replied. Here was a new aspect of the complex hierarchy of African society that we wished to explore. "Where did you get the Bushmen?" "They wandered in out of the bush." "How much do you pay them?" "Pay Bushmen? Hah. They are glad to work for me. If they are my Bushmen nobody stones them." It occurred to us that this verged somewhat on slavery, but we decided that the United Nations would prefer not to hear of it.

These were the people who produced the Michelangelo of primitive artists who painted the famous giraffe of the Nswatugi cave high in the Matopo hills. These were the hunters who could follow a wounded eland over the Kalahari day after day. These knew the lore of the deserts and wild animals as did no other people. But in contact with Bantu agriculturalists they became serfs at best. Once the tribal elder who knew where to find the tsama melons with their precious liquid, who knew how to use a sand well and how to make arrow poison has gone, the system breaks down. One wonders if it could not be arranged, somehow, that those who are left, the few in the desert and the recently discovered river Bushmen who hid out until now, could be left alone. Our world brings them only sadness and death.

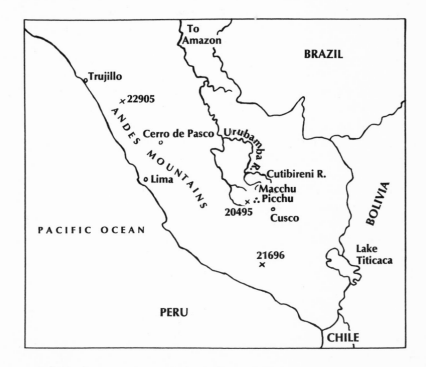

In 1963 the National Geographic Society sponsored an expedition into a little-known wilderness in the Vilcabamba Cordillera north of Cuzco in Peru. Subsequent studies by Peruvians and Americans have led to the proposal that a large wilderness national park, the Cutibireni park, be established here. Living in this region are groups of Machiguenga Indians, who have had little contact with European civilization. They do not appear to want further contact. Is there some good reason why their wishes cannot be respected? Further south in the Mato Grosso state of Brazil lives the Erigbaatsa tribe of Indians. They are completely primitive and do not know that there is a country called Brazil. I cannot see how they would benefit from the knowledge. Scattered through Latin America, Africa, Australia and Southeast Asia are similiar groups. Surely we are not still driven by the primitive compulsion to Christianize and civilize them all? We do not need to disturb the Gibson Desert or Arnhem Land, to bring enlightenment to Petén and Irian. If we do succeed, as we seem to be trying to, in blowing ourselves up in a nuclear war, these supposedly backward people may be the only hope of the human race. Even if we do not wipe ourselves out, if we simply tie ourselves up in technological knots and create a world we cannot tolerate, the presence of people who are not involved can help us find our way out. If we should, perchance, avoid both these perils, and tomorrow set to work to build a sane human society, there will be time then to improve the lot of people everywhere while still maintaining those differences that are of value. It took a million years for the diversity in human types and ways of life to evolve. Is our new-found and largely untested knowledge to bring with it such delusions of grandeur that we must destroy this wider human heritage?

No island can be completely undisturbed in our age.

Off in the Indian Ocean is an island group called Aldabra. It lies southwest of the Seychelles and northeast of Madagascar. As islands go these are nothing spectacular, a ring atoll of four smaller islands surrounding a lagoon, twenty miles long and perhaps three miles across the widest island. What makes Aldabra unusual in this world is that it is virtually undisturbed. No island can be completely undisturbed in our age, but Aldabra has not much in the way of soil, little potable water, no minerals or guano deposits of consequence, and generally nothing to attract the passerby. Consequently most things on Aldabra are much as they were before man ventured into the Indian Ocean.

One of its unique features is a large population of the giant tortoise, one of the few reptiles that colonize and survive on

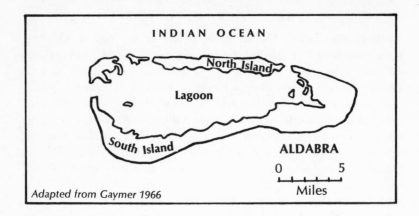

Adapted from Gaymer 1966

oceanic islands. It is estimated that there are around thirty-three thousand of these creatures on Aldabra and thus they are better established than their more famous relatives on the Galápagos Islands off South America. However, they once occurred also on Reunion and Mauritius, in the Seychelles and most of the Indian Ocean islands. Elsewhere they have been eliminated. On Aldabra they survive.

Along with the tortoise the island had some bats, including an endemic form of the large fruit bat or flying fox, and several lizards. It has a number of birds. The dodo didn't reach Aldabra, but there is a flightless rail that is probably extinct elsewhere, a flamingo, sacred ibis, some attractive pigeons and doves, weaver birds, sunbirds, bulbuls, drongos and even a falcon. There are breeding colonies of seabirds, including a major colony of frigate birds. All of these share the woodlands and grasslands, which are in their way unusual since they have not been changed much by man. All considered there is a unique ecosystem here, not like any place else.

It would seem that such a rare gem as Aldabra would have been set aside as a reserve and preserved for the future for scientific study and some limited public viewing as an example of what an island could be. We managed to get along thus far without it; its absence has not impeded our technological process—surely we could get along without it in the future?

But Great Britain has been having difficult times since it decided that colonialism belonged to the past. Pushed from the

A program to preserve the islands is underway. Hawaii Volcanoes National Park. (*Photograph courtesy of National Park Service*)

various corners of the earth by the upsurge of nationalism in its old domain, it is looking for places where a toehold can be held, here and there, without shouts of imperialism being, raised in the United Nations. Recently, with its base at Aden about to join the list of lost possessions, it has sought a new place for airfields, radar and similar installations somewhere in the Indian Ocean among the scattered remnants of the old empire. Perhaps not strangely, uninhabited Aldabra came to mind. Plans are now underway to bring Aldabra and its tortoises into the twentieth century. Nothing much can help the islands if the air base comes. There will be talk about setting up a nature reserve and good intentions about restricting development. But such good intentions have not helped the other islands and birds do get in the way of jet planes. As Roger Gaymer, who has described the island, has put it, our descendants will be able to go to Aldabra some day, read the old accounts and say "What an interesting place this must have *been!*"

On the other side of the world, in the West Indies, is an island called Dominica, which assumed in 1966 the new status of a self-governing Associated State in the British Commonwealth. Dominica is far from being uninhabited. Its 305 square miles supported an average of two hundred people to the square mile in 1962. However, for various reasons, much of its mountainous interior has been spared from exploitation; and its shoreline has not yet experienced the uniform spread of tourist-oriented resorts and hotels. It is rated by those who know the Caribbean as the last and the best of the high islands. Its tropical vegetation and animal life have attracted major attention from scientists of the Smithsonian Institution and its preservation is of concern to all who have an interest in island life or tropical ecology. But new governments need money, so in 1967 arrangements are being made and contracts signed to log off the native forests for lumber and pulp, without provision for reserving any area to be natural and undisturbed. Dominica is starting down the pathway so many others have followed, toward a future of overcrowding in a deteriorating land.

The preservation of places that are unusual and relatively unchanged by man should be a subject of international concern. Virgin Islands National Park. (*Photograph courtesy of National Park Service*)

Once every five years scientists from the Pacific nations gather for the Pacific Science Congress. In 1966 the 11th Congress was held in Tokyo, where several sessions were devoted to the problem of vanishing natural areas and wild species in the Pacific region. A resolution passed by the Congress read:

"In view of the unique significance for world science of a number of islands in the Pacific Ocean which have hitherto, wholly or in part, escaped man-made changes, and in view of the irreplaceable endemic or rare species for which some of these islands form last refuges, and of the serious threats to the continuance of such natural conditions for research, the Congress *affirms* the urgent international importance of securing early and effective conservation of natural habitats on such islands, and

RESOLVED to request member organizations of the Pacific Science Association to bring to the attention of their governments the need to exercise the strictest restraint in relation to such island natural areas, and

RESOLVED to request all scientists concerned to accord the fullest cooperation to the International Biological Programme and to the International Union for Conservation of Nature and Natural Resources in developing jointly with the Pacific Science Association surveys and recommendations which will enable the authorities concerned to establish an adequate permanent series of natural habitats conserved as a base for research throughout the Pacific region."

Resolutions buy no real estate, but this is a first step toward preserving the unique and the unusual in areas that have not yet been drastically changed by man. There are not many islands left in the Pacific or elsewhere that fit this category. We can hardly afford to lose any of them. At the present time the International Biological Programme is organizing a worldwide inventory of natural areas and wild species that are in need of preservation for the benefit of science, in hope of maintaining some of the natural variety that was part of the world inherited by the human race. The International Union for Conservation of Nature (IUCN) will cooperate and carry forward these efforts toward preservation. However, much more is needed. Effective participation of world governments, and not just their biologists and conservationists, is needed if the job is to be done. Even the smallest and least affluent of nations could do its bit for the world community in this effort.

At a time when the United Nations wastes much effort in acrimonious debate over areas about which they can do nothing effective, it would appear that something could be gained by turning to areas in which progress could be made and cooperation effected. The preservation of things that are different, unusual, of interest and concern to all who are aware of their values is such an activity. A worldwide commitment to the preservation of natural diversity would be one United Nations activity that the twenty-first century would be certain to appreciate. Perhaps the most vital first step would be to agree to leave alone, protect and

We need some places that are not crowded—where solitude in contact with nature can still be found. (*Photograph by Bob Hoke, courtesy of National Park Service*)

maintain those islands that have thus far escaped change. These
are the most endangered, since it takes so little to destroy them.

The concept of a World Heritage Trust was discussed at a
meeting on international cooperation held at the White House
in 1966. Such a trust would represent the international concern
and responsibility for outstanding areas of natural beauty, wild
undisturbed habitat, rare species of plants and animals. Obvious
areas that are candidates for such a trust can be thought of
quickly: Yellowstone, Serengeti National Park, Albert National
Park, the Kaziranga Sanctuary of the Indian rhinoceros in Assam,
the Udjung Kulon Game Reserve in Java, the Galápagos Islands,
Cutibireni, Aldabra, and so on. A list of areas can be provided by
the International Biological Programme and by IUCN, but a
beginning should be made early. Involved in the formation of such
a trust is an international agreement to maintain and preserve
these areas in accordance with the highest standards to be
specified by the international community. Such a trust could be
the repository of both government and private funds and a
vehicle for channeling financial aid to nations that cannot at
present manage the expense of providing adequate protection
for their outstanding natural areas.

Now that the technologically advanced nations are pouring
money and advice into those countries that are not technologically advanced in order to improve the economic welfare
of their peoples, another step in the area of international cooperation could be extremely useful. This would be directed toward
islands also, but the aim would be not preservation as such but
development along the soundest possible lines. We are constantly
being told that our scientists, technologists, economists, architects, city planners and other experts could, if given proper
backing, create a veritable heaven on earth; yet nowhere on
earth do we find any man-made Eden. I am certain that the
inhabitants of some of the world's islands would be willing to
have their lands converted into the earthly pa. ses that have
been promised for us all. Aid of various sorts and technical assistance can be sent for decades to Asia, Latin America or Africa,
without anyone knowing for sure at the end what was accom-
plished, what was really effective and what failed, what could

Some remote places should remain remote.

have happened if things had been done differently. The situations involved are too complex. By channeling only part of this assistance to some islands large enough to have variety, but small enough for accomplishments to become evident quickly, we could really test and demonstrate our ability. An international demonstration islands program could provide us a model for efforts in larger, more complex situations.

We pretend to much knowledge about city planning and development. Let's assemble an international team to do the best possible job on New Caledonia perhaps, Fiji, Barbados or the Azores, wherever the people are willing to let them try. We have technical experts in agriculture, forestry and all the land-use skills, experts on economic development, anthropology and sociology. It would take an integrated effort to produce anything of value that was fully viable. Surely it would be worthwhile to try, to give adequate financial support to provide the best possible effort?

Such a program might well reveal major weaknesses and deficiencies in our knowledge and skill. But would it not be better to find these out soon, in an area where results could be seen relatively quickly and viewed in the context of a complete ecosystem before we build many more Brasilias or go much further toward reshaping the life of the millions who crowd into Calcutta?

There is an intriguing area for international competition involved, if Russia and its Communist allies build a Communist paradise on some islands while other nations seek to build a capitalistic Eden elsewhere.

There is one final proposal that I would suggest here toward international efforts aimed at preserving or creating diversity on earth. It is in some ways the most important, and yet least likely to be implemented. This is an international agreement to leave people alone. If people want help, if they care to join the technological world, then by all means let us do what we can to aid and welcome them. But for those people who do not know the technological world exists, and for those who know, but would prefer to forget it, let us have a solemn compact that they will be permitted to go their own way, in peace. We have forsworn colonialism on an international scale, let us next agree internationally to allow peoples who are different the same freedom to keep to their own ways.

10

Planning Against Progress

We thought we were done with these things but
    we were wrong.
We thought, because we had power, we had wisdom,
We thought the long train would run to the end
    of Time.
We thought the light would increase.
Now the long train stands derailed and the bandits
    loot it.
Now the boar and the asp have power in our time.
Now the night rolls back on the West and the night
    is solid.

                        —Stephen Vincent Benét

Ꙭ I T A L L semed rather simple during the 1930s, there was the Depression and there was the issue of socialism. The Depression was caused by too much or too little socialism. One could march and shout "Red Front," or one could call out the National Guard and put down the rebels. But then there was Hitler and World War II, and we knew that the important thing was to win the war. After that we would straighten out the injustices and all would be well. There was the new hope of the United Nations but then there was Korea. If you were an African or an Asian in the 1950s the issues were clear cut, the call was for Freedom. But freedom came and all the old problems remained, or got worse.

We were going to feed the hungry, but there are two hungry mouths where once there was one. We were going to end war, but the wars are endless. We had faith in our science and it has given us the means to reach the moon, which is lifeless, and the means to make the earth lifeless too. We could not be blamed for despair, but each day the sun rises, and forests grow, and somewhere streams run clear. We can still hope. We have the tools now to build a better world, but we were not told the dimensions of the job, we were led to believe it was easy.

What happens next is in the long run a question of our goals and aspirations and our willingness to work. We could go on along our present lines, and assuming that we survived at all, which is doubtful, we might succeed in reaching our apparent objective —a uniform, technologically controlled world in which further change would be impossible. Or we could strive for another objective, for a different kind of country, one in which there was room for varied, diverse people living in varied and diverse ways in varied and diverse environments. Whether or not we can reach it depends upon how we decide about other matters.

There is the question of war. Are we willing to forego this luxury and to cease spending fifty to seventy or more billions of dollars each year in killing people, preparing to kill people and keeping people from killing us? If so, we had better be prepared to build the kind of international organization that will do the

We were going to feed the hungry, but there are two mouths where once there was one.

job. The United Nations, as presently constituted, obviously cannot. Since it is now generally agreed that nuclear war will not have victors, only, at best, survivors; that it will wipe out the civilizations of its participants; that it is likely to destroy the human race, we can surely question whether any alternative to it might not be more acceptable. Eliminating war will not happen tomorrow, no matter how good our intentions, and while we are working on this big problem we had better tackle others that are related.

There is the question of population. What are our goals? Over much of the underdeveloped world people are still behaving as though the world was young and there was plenty of room. Their rates of population increase, balanced against their environment and economy, suggest that they are striving toward a goal of a maximum number of people supported at a minimum level of subsistence. In many places this goal has been achieved and people live next to famine, but through massive effort each year the subsistence level is raised a little, and populations can continue to grow.

In our country we behave as though the important element was the ratio between population growth and our indices of economic activity. So long as economic production increases faster than our population there are those who feel that all is well. That the end result will be the standardized technological society where all efforts are aimed at the production of material things for a maximum population, we are not told. We are not told that all questions of value must be set aside except for those quantitative values suited to economic analysis. That even in this technological world population growth must someday be halted, and by then there will be no way out.

There is a general rule about populations that those concerned with humans often forget. All range and livestock managers, wild-life managers, field biologists or ecologists know that the important thing is habitat. If you protect the habitat, the range, the environment, the future of the population is relatively secure. If you allow the habitat to be destroyed, the population will cease to exist. Unfortunately, looking at things in this way requires a reversal of our humanitarian attitudes.

In the conservation of African wildlife, the humanitarian approach still has wide appeal to the general public. This has been to establish a national park in which the animals will be completely protected. No individual animal is allowed to be shot, snared or injured by man. Some national park protectors allow their humanitarian instincts to go further. Seeing a hunting dog or hyena bring down an antelope, they have tried and condemned him as one might a human murderer. Thereafter the four-footed killers were fair game, in the interest of protecting the "innocent" —grazers or browsers. The consequences of this approach are now well known.

Freed from their enemies, game populations have increased to the point where they can and in places have destroyed their habitat. With nothing left to eat, they die. The humanitarian approach enters again at this point. We provide a famine relief project and bring in food, or we provide "technical assistance" and build water holes in dry areas to open up more food supplies for the use of game. If this is done, and nothing else, then the population increases to the new carrying capacity, destroys an even broader area of habitat and faces even more massive loss from famine. Park administrators know now that the old approach does not work. They know that if they protect the grass-feeder they must also protect the predator; they know that if a population in the past was controlled through predation by man, then it must continue to be controlled by man. They know it is better to be hardhearted toward the elephant, but tender toward his range. With that attitude, there is a future for elephants.

One of the features of a wildlife population that presses upon the carrying capacity of its habitat is that it becomes prey to accidents, to disease and to the physiological breakdowns that follow excessive stress. The humanitarian instinct is to care for the sick, mend the injured and thus build up to the massive loss that occurs when the habitat is destroyed.

With wild animals we know the habitat must come first. If too many elephants overgraze and destroy their habitat, there will be no place for any elephants. It is better to be hard-hearted toward the animal but tender toward his environment.

For reasons that are themselves complex, we believe that humanity is subject to different rules, that we live in a different biosphere, but we do not. Our medical humanitarianism has touched off our population explosions. Our willingness to feed the hungry provides that they will live to destroy more of their land and that there will be more hunger tomorrow and less hope. We will take time to learn that we should think first of the land, the human environment. If we protect that, we can preserve humanity. If it is destroyed, we will be destroyed with it.

The final choice in the population question is the one we must decide upon now, since each year's delay moves us farther away from the chance of achieving the goal. It would be a decision to level off our population at some more nearly optimum level, where we could still maintain the freedom, the diversity, the wilderness and open space, the many different ways of life that each one of us may desire. The question of what is an optimum population is one that has long been debated without any general agreement. Each nation and each culture will have its own ideas. I believe that in America and in the world we have long ago passed it and are moving farther away from it. Others would not agree, and the question is not yet worth arguing. At present if we can simply slow down and eventually halt population growth, we will be accomplishing a great deal. The year 2000 is a handy target date: if we can halt growth below the level of three hundred million Americans, we can then consider the possibility of slowing birth rates still more. By then we will have lost much, but with proper organization we could still have a diversified, interesting, free and open world.

Control of population growth rests upon individual decisions, and I hope we can keep it that way. We have all the devices and techniques for preventing births that we need to do the job. Obviously, they are being used since our birth rates continue to decline. Obviously, also, too many people think they can afford large families, since birth rates are not dropping fast enough. The question of whether or not an individual can afford to have four or more children is now irrelevant. The real question is whether America can afford it. The answer there is obvious. If we want a high quality of environment, if we want to slow down the race toward a uniform world, America cannot afford for individuals to have large families. Since family size is to a degree a matter of fashion in this country, it is particularly unfortunate that some of our national leaders, respected and followed by the younger generation, have not yet received the message and continue to reproduce as though they lived in pioneer America.

Considering only the questions of war, population and technology, any person who looked objectively at the world today: a world in which the United States, Russia, China, France and England all have a nuclear war machine that they will be permitted to use once, and only once, the most likely prospect for mankind is Armaggedon. Assuming we can avoid this we have the opportunity to strive in a different direction, to respect human differences, to protect the human environment, to provide for and encourage diversity. This is a hard road, a different one from what we have been following, but it is one that could lead to various Utopias and to space for people who cannot stand Utopias. There is no road map, but it is possible to point out some general directions. First we might take a look at the wrong direction, the one in which we have been going.

We could in theory at least let things go on as they have been. Populations would continue to increase and people would continue to move into the already congested cities. Detroit would continue to produce and sell unlimited numbers of gasoline burners, and state and federal governments would vie in their efforts to build bigger and better highways, including those around San Antonio, through the French Quarter of New Orleans, across San Francisco's waterfront and through its Golden Gate Park, through the redwoods, through Rock Creek Park in Washington, into Yellowstone and Yosemite, and on and on. Land speculators and real estate developers would vie with each other until our shorelines were lined with houses and suburbs sprawled in continuous strips from New York to Minneapolis, Seattle to San Diego. Pollution could go unchecked and all our rivers formed into efficient sewer systems. New industries could thrive manufacturing individual and home air purifiers and we could continue to use our skies as garbage dumps. We could forget that unpleasant, restrictive word called conservation, and con-

We could, in theory, let things go on as they have been. Suburbs could sprawl in continuous strips from Seattle to San Diego. (*Photograph courtesy of Soil Conservation Service*)

centrate on our *gross* national product, that index of our real, hard-cash level of well-being. We could hire bigger and better police forces and build bigger jails. We could establish ever more extensive mental institutions, and thus try to maintain our unrestricted, profit-motivated, free enterprise way of life.

Some years ago I might have written that to follow such a course would be madness. Now that is trite and obvious. We have been following it, and 10 to 20 per cent of our total population suffers from serious mental illness, or will so suffer during their lifetime. Madness does not discourage us.

It is generally agreed by most in positions of responsibility who have knowledge of our situation and its trend that we cannot continue as we have been going. It is also generally agreed that to change our course we must do more and better planning, develop a strategy to control and direct our future growth. It is agreed also that we must take the politico-economic action needed to implement the plans and the strategy. However, planning has been involved in some of our worst blunders. Our highways are planned. The planners just don't happen to take everything into account. Our cities mostly operate on some sort of plan and have zoning and other laws to help implement it. The suburbs still slurb and the slums grow stickier. Obviously we need something better. I would suggest a different way of planning with new priorities and criteria. It is really not new, but it is not practiced widely. I would call it planning against progress. It would clearly be planning against the mistakes that we make in the name of progress.

Planning must operate with a different set of values and priorities. We must recognize first that there are some things, qualities in our environment, that are irreplaceable. We must first of all plan to preserve the irreplaceables. We must secondly recognize that too much growth in any area will defeat the efforts of any planners. We must therefore plan to control growth.

In the nineteenth century and the early years of the twentieth, it was possible for leaders of government to take bold steps in the direction of planning against progress. They did not know at the time that they were doing it. The West was largely empty and the votes were mostly in the East. It took no great amount of political courage to block out large sections of the public lands in the West and say that these would be maintained as national parks or national forests. Who was upset? Only a few sheepherders and lumberjacks. The cost was minimal. The army could be moved in to police or patrol, or a few rangers could be hired for little money.

In the country behind the small city of Los Angeles, which had some fifty thousand people, the land that was to become the Angeles, San Bernardino, and Los Padres National Forests was set aside to protect the watersheds and the timber, and prevent fire and exploitation from ruining the rough mountain country. Today when eight million people crowd into the Los Angeles region the national forests still stand, largely free from any form of urban development, in places sufficiently undisturbed and wild to allow for a proposal to set aside a 150,000 acre wilderness area in the country north of the smog-ridden California metropolis. This was a form of land-use zoning by the

federal government. It said what would not be developed, and
with all of its minor failures and some major shortcomings it
has been kept intact. It has contained and controlled growth and
preserved some irreplaceable elements of natural diversity.

In 1872 when President Grant signed a bill setting aside some
two million acres as our first national park, the Yellowstone,
there was no great hue and cry about interference with private
enterprise or inhibition of the growth of the Wyoming Territory.
In fact it is doubtful if Congress and the President had any clear
understanding of what they were doing. Today Yellowstone
stands and despite a certain amount of hacking and construction
involved in accommodating its millions of visitors, most of it
is like it was in 1872. It stands as another monument against
progress, a form of federal zoning that has not been set aside.

Yellowstone is of course irreplaceable. It is also immovable. It
represents values and resources that cannot be found elsewhere.
It must be preserved in site or not at all. You can't build a city
there and find another place for the national park. There are
many such irreplaceables. They represent our natural areas and

Today Yellowstone still stands, most of it as it was in 1872—a monument
against progress, a form of federal zoning that has not been set aside.
Yellowstone is, of course, irreplaceable. It is also immovable—you can't
build a city there and find another place for the park. (*Photograph courtesy
of National Park Service*)

places of outstanding scenic beauty, the homes of rare forms of wildlife, the places where history was made, architectural or monumental masterpieces of man's own making.

The whooping cranes, the few that are left, return each winter to the Aransas. You can't build on Aransas and tell the cranes to park somewhere else. The site must be maintained if this vanishing species is to stay on earth. You cannot accommodate the values of the Everglades any place in the United States except the Everglades. These things are obvious, and we have recognized them in large part by setting these areas aside. We have yet, however, to recognize fully all of the ramifications involved in such a decision. You can't build a highway through a wilderness and still have a wilderness. You can't put a dam and reservoir in a wild canyon and still have a wild canyon. You have to continue to supply water to the Everglades. These are areas of conflict today, because they bring narrow-scope, short-range planning into conflict with broader-scope, longer-range values and goals.

We can thus move to the first objective for the new kind of

You can't put a dam in a wild canyon and still have a wild canyon. (*Photograph courtesy of Bureau of Reclamation*)

planning, the identification and preservation of the irreplaceables. On a national scale this represents the job that the National Park Service, the International Biological Programme and other agencies are now attempting to do. Those areas that are sufficiently distinctive and valuable to deserve federal attention must first be located. These include the areas of superlative quality that deserve national park status and the areas of wilderness quality that deserve inclusion in the wilderness preservation system. Included also are those homes of wild animals that require the degree of preservation represented by a federal wildlife refuge. But also included are representative areas of all of the undisturbed natural communities with their plant and animal life that need including in a national system of scientific reserves.

Planning for these areas must include the understanding that they will not be used for any purpose that conflicts with their primary value: not for dams, or highways, or exploitation.

Areas that do not require federal attention, but still are of major importance as recreation space, outdoor scenery or natural diversity to the citizens of a state, need including in a state system of parks, reserves or refuges of various kinds. Still other areas that are not of major significance to a state may yet be of great importance to the quality of living within a county, city or town and deserve inclusion in a local, open-space preservation system.

Putting these areas down on a map in a distinctive color to show that they must be preserved for all time is of course only a first step. It is a long time past the days of Theodore Roosevelt when Congress could simply decree the preservation of great areas of land. It can still be done with federal lands, but most of the nation and some of its more important areas are privately owned.

To take some small examples: In Humboldt County, California, is an area of unusual sand-dune vegetation unmatched elsewhere in the state. The federal government is concerned with the major area of the Oregon Dunes farther north and if they can manage to establish them as a national park or seashore they will have done their share. The state government should be interested, but the only area that remains largely undisturbed is small in size, and has somehow escaped the attention of the state park planners. The area has great scientific interest and has been studied by great numbers of ecology students, but it has limited recreational capacity at best. Sand-dune vegetation is easily disturbed and does not hold up to tourist trampling. The area is owned by an individual who would prefer to see it preserved in the future as he has saved it in the past. Yet he cannot afford to give it away.

Off the coast of Florida is an island that has been preserved in private ownership over many decades. It has unusual wildlife and natural vegetation, yet now it must be sold. The real estate developers, who have ruined much of the land in Florida, would love to have it. It would then be just like every other place. Who is to provide the several millions of dollars needed for its purchase? The Fahkahatchee Strand area of the Big Cypress Swamp in Florida is another area that many feel needs to be set aside as a unique example of a type of country not represented in the Everglades or elsewhere. But the National Park Service cannot be expected to fight every battle and it is having trouble enough now preserving some of the Islandia area of Biscayne Bay. Off

There are many small patches of wild or scenic country that need to be set aside. The federal government can't do it all.

the Virginia coast is a large, little-disturbed island of unusual quality. It too is an irreplaceable part of our natural heritage, perhaps not sufficiently distinctive for federal attention, but still distinctive. Unless it is set aside it will support another Ocean City in the future. These areas must be bought. They cannot reasonably be protected in any other way. Zoning could be tried by the appropriate authority in such cases—zoning against development, to preserve open space. If it could be made effective it would keep the developers out. But more likely it could be contested successfully in court, as discriminatory against the landowner.

Without doubt the greatest single obstacle to the implementation of planning against progress is not ignorance, not unawareness of natural values, but lack of cold cash. We took a step forward when the Land and Water Conservation Act was passed in 1963. Fees charged for the use of federal recreation areas were set aside in a fund available to state and local governments on a matching basis for purchase of conservation and recreation land. However, the amount of money that has been raised thus far is inadequate to the job. Taxes on cigarettes and real estate transfer have been used to acquire money for the purchase of parks and other open space lands, taxes on gasoline have been considered. But land prices everywhere are high and there is not enough money.

I suspect that the public would be more willing than Congress to see a larger share of the federal income budgeted for the purchase of parks, refuges and reserves, if they were to be told the whole story. Too many people assume that when Congress passes an act proclaiming an Assateague or Fire Island National Recreation Area that they have by that act acquired the land. Realization of the cost involved is seldom widespread. Congress itself is overly sensitive to pressure from the ever-alert special interest groups who see opportunities for profit or threats of loss in such land acquisition.

Congressmen, after all, like to be reelected. If they take a public-interest-above-all attitude, and "let the chips fall where they may," their terms in the legislature are short. The public, while approving, often has other things to do on election day; the private interests remember who pays off.

Fortunately the major job of acquiring areas of national park status in the United States has been to a large degree completed. In California, for example, there are only two major areas that deserve further attention: the Redwoods National Park and the Channel Islands. At least one of the large Channel Islands, Santa Rosa or Santa Cruz, should be acquired as a national park, since these are unique places that are likely to get the full, real estate development treatment if they are not watched. There are still many areas, however, that deserve federal consideration for protection as national scientific reserves, and an even greater number that require protection at the state or local open-space preservation level.

The United States has many odd bits of country that are still quite wild because nobody bothers with them or knows that they are there. Nevada, for example, is particularly rich in this

Santa Cruz, in the Channel Islands of California. Proposed for a national park. (*Photograph courtesy of National Park Service*)

Not wilderness, but wild country in Nevada, where the tourist as yet does not go.

kind of country. It doesn't quite qualify as wilderness, it is not sufficiently distinctive for a national park, yet it is quite delightful at the right time of year. Much of it is administered by the Bureau of Land Management. Cattle and sheep are grazed on it and there are mining claims here and there. The roads are rough and rugged and most highway drivers are afraid, with good reason, to try them. The worst thing that could happen to these areas is for them to receive publicity and good roads. Eventually this may happen, but I will not hasten the process. Planning against progress involves not building roads into wild country. National park administrators in particular, but also those in charge of other federal lands, should take this to heart. They should move with deliberate lack of haste in road building.

To move now from the question of natural areas and wild country to the other extreme of urban America, if we can accept Sam Zisman's rule: that urban open space is the fixed quality and

Roads can bring disruption. We should go slowly in planning new roads into wild country.

all other land uses are flexible, we will be on the way to planning against progress and thus creating viable cities. Two other rules seem necessary: that each community should have a size and population that is planned for and beyond which further growth is discouraged; and that each community should strive for its own distinctive character in order to preserve urban diversity.

The idea that each community should have a limit to growth seems so apparent that I cannot see why anyone questions it. Without such limits no plans can be made to stick. If you provide space and facilities for a population of one hundred thousand and then two hundred thousand move in, the system simply breaks down. If you patch up and add on to the older framework you begin to encounter the whole range of urban problems that plague us today, from traffic congestion and pollution to a general eroding of the identity and quality of the city. Admittedly you could get away from this in new cities. Many planners have come up with sound ideas for expansible cities, cities that are planned from the start to accommodate growth. If growth were desirable, such cities would be an approach to providing for it. But nobody has yet produced any evidence that continued growth is desirable. All the evidence seems to lie in the opposite direction, that the better quality of living will be found in the smaller city.

We already have our giant cities and they will remain. Some will prefer them and should have the choice. But nobody pretends New York would be better with twenty million people. Further growth should be accommodated elsewhere. The private developer is unlikely to provide a city any larger than James Rouse's Columbia. It is up to the federal government to do the larger job. It is up to it also to bring life back to the smaller towns of America as the Secretary of Agriculture, Orville Freeman, has emphasized, and part of this can be done by the awarding of federal contracts, the location of federal agencies and the like. I am told that Francisco Franco has managed to keep the towns and villages of Spain alive and thriving in just this way, but I have not seen the evidence personally.

Fortunately the federal government has taken the first hesitant step toward following the advice of Ian McHarg, Athelstan Spilhaus and the others who recommend new cities, by providing planning money for such a project to the University of Minnesota to establish a new city of a quarter million located well away from any existing urban center. It will be of great interest to follow the progress of this project. However, the size of the job should not be minimized.

We must, by the year 2000, provide housing and facilities of all kinds for perhaps one hundred million more Americans, unless people are far more sensible about birth control than they have been. Some seventy-five million of these can be expected to become urbanites, unless encouraged to go elsewhere. This could mean the building of the equivalent of one hundred and fifty new cities of a half million population each, an average of three for each state in the Union. I do not know how much these would cost. England is building a new town in the northeast that will cost 280 million dollars and accommodate eighty thousand people. We could assume at least 5 billion dollars for a city to

All places need not be alike and at odds with their environment. It is possible to build places that are different, that take advantage of their natural surroundings.

accommodate a half million. This means we could only afford to
build fifteen such cities next year with the amount of money we
will spend next year on war and defense. It might take our war
and defense budget for the next ten years, with a few space
rockets thrown in, to build our one hundred and fifty new cities.
Of course we can't afford it. We can only afford other kinds of
activities.

The problem of making each city distinctive and different
obviously is at odds with our present methods of building. It is
cheaper and safer to repeat a pattern, and we have been doing
this the world over. Some cities and towns have deliberately
sought to maintain a character that was built up in an earlier
period, but even they have had only qualified success. Santa
Fe has its old Spanish-Pueblo section, but has been unable to
prevent its new developments from looking just like Fresno,
California, or Columbus, Ohio. Tucson evidently gave up the
battle long ago since even its downtown section is a conglomerate
American-style mess. Annapolis, Maryland, has managed to maintain a distinctive character; Williamsburg is obviously a special
case; Santa Barbara, California, has had only partial success.

Obviously what is needed is a sense of civic pride that is able
to override some supposedly more practical considerations; a
willingness to give greater scope to architects; an ability to take
into consideration the natural history of the setting and build in
accordance with it. There is no reason why a desert city should
not be built in accord with and to take advantage of its desert
scenery and climate, why a mountain town should not be at least
as well adapted to its environment as its equivalent in Switzer-
land or Austria. In some parts of the country the environment
is benevolent and the city can be open; in other parts the climate
is hostile during much of the year and the city need close itself
off to a degree. The results of such efforts could be enormously
beneficial to those who dwell in cities; they might go a long way
to restoring some meaning to the words urbane and civilized.

Planning against progress involves not providing facilities for
growth where growth is undesirable, and of planning facilities
where growth is wanted. This is a function of government. It
would involve halting growth in Seattle-Tacoma and perhaps en-

couraging it in Wenatchee or Missoula, stopping it in Denver and encouraging it in Cheyenne, stopping it in San Francisco and Los Angeles and encouraging it at Eureka, Redding or perhaps Bishop. It would involve discouraging the builder from putting up the standard high-rise, or suburb, and encouraging him to put up something distinctive, fitting the character of the city and the land.

Planning against progress means planning a city so that the need for private transportation will be minimized; it means not building the freeway that will destroy some area of civic beauty, civic pride or living space; it means protecting the historical site or architectural masterpiece even though the land would bring in higher taxes with an office building or apartment house.

Planning against progress means protecting our orchards, vineyards and other prime agricultural lands against urban development. It means zoning that the community is willing to stand by; it means refusal to provide services to undesirable subdivisions. It means a willingness to spend money and to forego income that might otherwise be available.

The willingness to spend money is the key factor. It has been the obstacle on the road to a better environment. But it is less of an obstacle now. All of us have been willing to spend a fair share of our income in providing ourselves with a decent place to live. Now, however, it is not enough to buy a house, we must also buy an environment to put it in. There is no point in establishing an architectural dream house in a place where the air is not fit to breathe and the water is polluted. There is no point in buying an expensive car if there is no place we can drive. The old American system of destructive exploitation made sense to the individual so long as there was a better place for him to go when he had made his money destroying or polluting a local environment. Now that we are all forced to drink our own sewage and live in the squalor that we create, the willingness to buy a better kind of world is becoming more widespread.

There is no way from here to paradise. The Garden of Eden has been left behind, but here somewhere on the far side of Eden we may yet create a more livable world. We cannot build the perfect world and if we could we would probably tire of it, since we are imperfect beings. We are various in our aspirations and the best we can hope for is a varied world. I would not want to design a Utopia and then be forced to live in it; at least I would want access to other people's Utopias. Therefore I believe that the way out for us must lie in a deliberate effort to maintain and build diversity, so that in each section of this land there will be a different kind of country, with its different wilderness and wild lands, its characteristic farmlands and rural landscapes, its varied cities that contain room for varied peoples. We have the power, the technology and the wealth with which to do this. We need only the will.

References

CHAPTER 1

Borgstrom, Georg. *The Hungry Planet*. New York: Macmillan, 1965.
Calder, Ritchie. "Freedom Begins with Breakfast," *Freedom from Hunger*, 7, No. 45 (1966): 8-11. Rome: F.A.O.
Darling, F. Fraser, and John Milton. *The Future Environment of North America*. New York: Natural History Press, 1966.
Food and Agricultural Organization. *FAO/Industry Cooperative Program*. Mimeographed. Rome, 1966.
Jung, Carl. *The Undiscovered Self*. Boston: Atlantic-Little, Brown, 1957.
Leopold, Aldo. *A Sand County Almanac*. New York: Oxford University Press, 1949.
Morison, Samuel E. *The Oxford History of the American People*. New York: Oxford University Press, 1965.
Wilkinson, John. *The Quantitative Society or What Are You to Do with Noodle?* Santa Barbara, Calif.: Center for the Study of Democratic Institutions, 1964.

CHAPTER 2

Brooks, C. E. P. *Climate Through the Ages*. London: Ernest Benn, 1949.
Conway, R. G. *Crop Pest Control and Resource Conservation in Tropical Southeast Asia*. Proceedings of Conference on Conservation of Nature and Natural Resources in Tropical Southeast Asia. Unassembled. Mimeographed. Bangkok, 1965.
Darling, F. Fraser (ed.). *Implications of the Rising Carbon Dioxide Content of the Atmosphere*. Washington, D.C.: Conservation Foundation, 1963.
Desmond, Annabelle. "Low Birth Rates of European Catholic Countries," *Population Bulletin*, 18, No. 2 (1962): 28-32.
Desmond, Annabelle, and J. K. Morris. "The Story of Mauritius," *Population Bulletin*, 18, No. 5 (1962): 93-115.
Finch, V. C., and G. T. Trewartha. *Elements of Geography*. 2d ed.

New York: McGraw-Hill, 1942.

Gleason, H. A., and A. Cronquist. *The Natural Geography of Plants.* New York: Columbia University Press, 1964.

Hesse, R., W. C. Allee, and K. P. Schmidt. *Ecological Animal Geography.* New York: John Wiley, 1937.

Holdridge, L. R. Determination of World Plant Formations from Simple Climatic Data, *Science,* 195 (1947):367-368.

Mumford, Lewis. *The Transformations of Man.* New York: Collier Books, 1956.

Poleman, Thomas T. *The Papaloapan Project.* Stanford, Calif.: Stanford University Press, 1964.

Richards, P. W. *The Tropical Rain Forest.* New York: Cambridge University Press, 1952.

Sauer, Carl O. "Status and Change in the Rural Midwest—A Retrospect," *Mitteilungen der Osterreichischen Geographischen Gessellschaft,* 105, No. 3 (1963):357-365.

Stevenson-Hamilton, J. *Animal Life in Africa.* New York: E. P. Dutton, 1912.

Walker, H. J. "Overpopulation in Mauritius: A Survey." *Geographical Review,* 54, No. 2 (1964):243-248.

CHAPTER 3

Ardrey, Robert. *The Territorial Imperative.* New York: Atheneum, 1966.

Clark, J. Desmond. *Prehistory of Southern Africa.* Harmondsworth, England: Penguin, 1959.

Darling, F. Fraser. "The Ecological Approach to the Social Sciences," *American Scientist,* 39, No. 2 (1951):244-254.

Goodall, Jane. "My Life among Wild Chimpanzees," *National Geographic,* 124, No. 2 (1963):272-308.

Hawkes Jacquetta. *Man on Earth.* New York: Random House, 1953.

Jung, Carl G. *Psychological Types.* Translated by H. Godwin Baynes. London: Pantheon Books, 1923.

Mumford, Lewis. "Closing Statement," in *Future Environments of North America.* New York: Natural History Press, 1966.

Parks, George B. (ed.). *The Book of Ser Marco Polo, the Venetian.*

New York: Book League of America, 1930.

Sauer, Carl O. "The Agency of Man on Earth," in *Man's Role in Changing the Face of the Earth*. Chicago: University of Chicago Press, 1956.

——. *Agricultural Origins and Dispersal*. New York: American Geographical Society, 1952.

Stewart, Omer C. "Fire as the First Great Force Employed by Man," in *Man's Role in Changing the Face of the Earth*. Chicago: University of Chicago Press, 1956.

CHAPTER 4

American Forest Products Industries, Inc. *Our Growing Redwoods*. Washington, D.C.: A.F.P.I., 1965.

Butcher, Russell D. "Ravaged Land or a Redwood National Park?" *Defenders of Wildlife News*, July 1965, pp. 33-38.

——. "Redwoods Face a Race against Time," *Audubon*, July–August 1965, pp. 234-239.

California Forest Industries Committee. *An Analysis of Logging and the 1965 California Floods*. San Francisco: Calif. Forest Ind. Comm., 1965.

Cooper, D. W. *The Coast Redwood—Will It Survive?* Berkeley: University of California Agriculture Extension Service, 1964.

Craig, James B. "How Private Are Private Lands?" *American Forests*, 17, No. 12 (1965):14-17.

——. "Living Ghosts of the Inyos," *ibid.*, 72, No. 12 (1966):14-17.

——. "The Redwood Pot Begins to Boil," *ibid.*, 72, No. 1 (1966): 39, 55-57.

Draper, William H., Jr. "Parks or More People?" *National Parks Magazine*, 40, No. 223 (1966):10-13.

Harlow, W. M., and E. S. Harrar. *Textbook of Dendrology*. 2d ed. New York: McGraw-Hill, 1941.

Hudson, Lois P. Logging for Floods, *Nation*, May 17, 1965, 531-533.

Mather, Deane B., and Rudolf W. Becking. *The Timber Economy of Humboldt County, California in 1968*. Mimeographed. 1965.

Moss, Frank E., "Why I'm for a Department of Natural Resources," *American Forests*, 72, No. 3 (1966):16-17, 46.

National Park Service. *The Redwoods*. Washington, D.C.: National Park Service, 1964.

Vaux, Henry J. *Timber in Humboldt County*. Bulletin 748. Berkeley: University of California Agriculture Experimental Station, 1955.

CHAPTER 5

Barnes, Irston R. "Threatened Wilderness Areas in the Great Smokies," *Atlantic Naturalist*, **21**, No. 1 (1966):3-4.

Brandborg, Stewart. "On the Carrying Capacity of Wilderness," *Living Wilderness*, **82** (1963):28-33.

Brookfield, C. M., and O. Griswold. *They All Called It Tropical*. Miami, Fla.: Data Press, 1964.

Craig, James B. "A Look at the North Cascades," *American Forests*, **72**, No. 3 (1966):12-14, 47.

Douglas, William O. "The North Cascades: National Resource of the Future," *Sierra Club Bulletin*, **50**, No. 10 (1965):10-11.

———. *A Wilderness Bill of Rights*. Boston: Little, Brown, 1965.

Farb, Peter. "Disaster Threatens the Everglades," *Audubon*, **67**, No. 5 (1965):302-309.

Finn, Melvin A. "Humans, Plants and Animals in Florida's Fahkahatchee Strand," *National Parks Magazine*, **40**, No. 226 (1966): 10-13.

Gilligan, James. "The Wilderness Resources," in *Tomorrow's Wilderness*. San Francisco: Sierra Club, 1963.

Gresham, Grits. "Marco Island. Model for Developers," *National Wildlife*, **5**, No. 2 (1967):4-9.

Hudson, Lois. "The Benevolent Wreckers," *Nation*, April 4, 1966, pp. 393-396.

Kuchler, A. W. *Potential Natural Vegetation of the Conterminous United States*. Special Publication 36. New York: American Geographical Society, 1964.

Leopold, Aldo. *A Sand County Almanac*. New York: Oxford University Press, 1949.

Lucas, Robert C. "Wilderness Perception and Use: The Example of the Boundary Waters Canoe Area," *Natural Resource Journal*, **3**, No. 3 (1964):394-411.

Nadel, Michael (ed.). "A Handbook on the Wilderness Act," Special Issue No. 86, *The Living Wilderness.*

———. "North Cascades Report," *Living Wilderness,* **29,** (1966): 33-39.

Nash, Hugh. "Storm over the Grand Canyon," *Parks and Recreation,* June 1966, pp. 497-500.

North Cascades Study Team. *The North Cascades.* Washington, D.C.: Department of the Interior, 1965.

Outdoor Recreation Resources Review Commission. *Outdoor Recreation for America.* Washington, D.C., 1962.

Platt, Rutherford. *Wilderness.* New York: Dodd, Mead & Co., 1961.

Shelford, Victor E. *The Ecology of North America.* Urbana: University Illinois Press, 1963.

Sierra Club. "North Cascades National Park Officially Proposed," *Sierra Club Bulletin,* February 1966, pp. 3-6.

———. "Support Grows for a North Cascades National Park," *ibid.,* March 1966, pp. 17-18.

Smith, Anthony Wayne. "An Analysis of the North Cascades Study Report," *National Parks Magazine,* (1966): p. 2.

———. "The North Cascades," *ibid.,* **40,** No. 223 (1966):2.

———. "The Shame of the Everglades," *ibid.,* **39,** No. 215 (1965): 2, 20.

Straight, Michael. "The Water Picture in Everglades National Park," *ibid.,* **39,** No. 215 (1965): 4-9.

Robertson, William B., Jr. *Everglades—the Park story.* Coral Gables, Fla.: University of Miami Press, 1959.

Tebeau, C. W. *They Lived in the Park.* Coral Gables, Fla.: University of Miami Press, 1963.

Zim, Herbert S. *A Guide to the Everglades National Park and the Nearby Florida Keys.* New York: Golden Press, 1960.

CHAPTER 6

Banfield, A. W. F. *The Mammals of Banff National Park, Alberta.* Bulletin 159. Ottawa: National Museum of Canada, 1958.

Bartlett, H. H. "Fire, Primitive Agriculture, and Grazing in the Tropics," in *Man's Role in Changing the Face of the Earth.* Chicago: University of Chicago Press, 1956.

Commoner, Barry. *Science and Survival.* New York: Viking, 1966.

Department of Northern Affairs and National Resources. *Wisdom's Heritage—The National Parks of Canada.* Ottawa, 1961.

Dufresne, Frank. "Plight of the Ice Bear," *Audubon,* 68, No. 6 (1966):418-425.

Fuller, W. A. *The Biology and Management of the Bison of Wood Buffalo National Park.* Ottawa: Canadian Wildlife Service, 1962.

Leopold, Aldo. *A Sand County Almanac.* New York: Oxford University Press, 1949.

Leopold, A. Starker. "Adios, Gavilán," *Pacific Discovery,* 2, No. 1 (1949):4-13.

———. *Wildlife of Mexico.* Berkeley: University of California Press, 1959.

Leopold, A. Starker, and F. Fraser Darling. *Wildlife in Alaska.* New York: Conservation Foundation and Ronald Press, 1953.

Murie, Adolf. "The Wolves of Mount McKinley," in *Fauna of the National Parks of the United States.* Fauna Series No. 5. Washington, D.C.: Department of the Interior, 1944.

Woodwell, George M. "Toxic Substances and Ecological Cycles," *Scientific American,* 216, No. 3 (1967):24-31.

CHAPTER 7

Allen, Frederick Lewis. *The Big Change.* New York: Bantam Classics, 1961.

Alonson, William.."The Historic and the Structural Theories of Urban Form: Their Implication for Urban Renewal," *Land Economics,* 40, No. 2 (1964):227-231.

Gordon, Mitchell. *Sick Cities.* Baltimore: Penguin, 1965.

Gruen, Victor. *The Heart of Our Cities.* New York: Simon and Schuster, 1964.

Handlin, Oscar. "The New Urban Society," *Ekistics,* 20, No. 120 (1965):253-255.

Hoyt, Homer. "Growth and Structure of Twenty-one Great World Cities," *Land Economics,* 42, No. 1 (1966): 53-64.

Jacobs, Jane. *The Death and Life of Great American Cities.* New York: Random House, 1965.

Lynch, Kevin, *The Image of the City*. Cambridge, Mass.: M.I.T. Press, 1960.

Piel, Gerald, ed. *Cities*. New York: Alfred A. Knopf, 1965.

Reisman, David. *The Lonely Crowd*. New Haven, Conn.: Yale University Press, 1950.

Tuchman, Barbara. *The Proud Tower*. New York: Macmillan, 1966.

Whyte, William H. *Cluster Development*. New York: American Conservation Association, 1964.

CHAPTER 8

Ardrey, Robert. *The Territorial Imperative*. New York: Atheneum, 1966.

Bowden, Lord. "Expectations for Science. 1. To the Limits of Growth," *New Scientist*, **27**, No. 463 (1965):849-853.

Bresler, Jack (ed.). *Human Ecology*. Reading, Mass.: Addison-Wesley, 1966.

Brown, Harrison. *The Challenge of Man's Future*. New York: Viking, 1954.

Burrough, Roy. "Should Urban Land Be Publicly Owned?" *Land Economics*, **42**, No. 1 (1966):11-20.

Calhoun, John. "Population Density and Social Pathology," *Scientific American*, **206** (1962):139-148.

Cousins, Norman (ed.). *Freedom to Breathe*. Report of the Mayor's Task Force. New York, 1966.

Dasmann, Raymond F. *The Destruction of California*. New York: Macmillan, 1965.

Duhl, Leonard (ed.). *The Urban Condition*. New York: Basic Books, 1963.

Darling, F. Fraser, and John Milton (eds.). *The Future Environments of North America*. New York: Natural History Press, 1966.

Eckardt, Wolf von. "The Age of Anti-Architecture," *Ekistics*, **20**, No. 120 (1965):270-272.

Farness, Sanford. "Man in Tyrannopolis: The City Is Dying," *Panorama, Chicago Daily News*, April 30, 1966, p. 3.

Gordon, Mitchell. *Sick Cities*. Baltimore: Penguin, 1965.

Gottmann, Jean. "Megalopolis, or the Urbanization of the Northeastern

Seaboard," *Economic Geography*, July 1957.

Gruen, Victor. *The Heart of Our Cities*. New York: Simon and Schuster, 1964.

Hall, Edward T. *The Hidden Dimension*. New York: Doubleday and Co., 1966.

Hall, Peter. *The World Cities*. New York: McGraw-Hill, 1966.

Jacobs, Jane. *The Death and Life of Great American Cities*. New York: Random House, 1965.

Hoyt, Homer. "Growth and Structure of Twenty-one Great World Cities," *Land Economics*, **42**, No. 1 (1966):53-64.

Hawkes, Jacquetta. *Man on Earth*. New York: Random House, 1953.

Lorenz, Konrad. *On Aggression*. New York: Harcourt, Brace & World, 1966.

Lynch, Kevin. *The Image of the City*. Cambridge, Mass.: M.I.T. Press, 1960.

Mangiamele, Joseph. "A Positive Approach to Population Distribution: A Case for Reversing the Trends," *Land Economics*, **42**, No. 1 (1966):117-124.

McHarg, Ian L. "Ecological Determinism," in *Future Environments of North America*. New York: Natural History Press, 1966.

McLuhan, Marshall. *Understanding Media: The Extensions of Man*. New York, McGraw-Hill Paperback, 1965.

Middleton, J. T. "Man and His Habitat: Problems of Pollution." *Bulletin of Atomic Scientists*, **21**, No. 3 (1965):5.

Montgomery, Roger. Comment on "Fear and the House-as-Haven in the Lower Class," *Journal of the American Institute of Planners*, **32**, No. 1 (1966):31-37.

Mumford, Lewis. *The City in History*. New York: Harcourt, Brace & World, 1961.

Rainwater, Lee. "Fear and the House-as-Haven in the Lower Class," *Journal of the American Institute of Planners*, **32**, No. 1 (1966): 23-31.

Rudduck, Grenfell. "Planning for National Redevelopment," *Planning Institute Journal* (Canberra), **3**, No. 3 (1965):79-83.

Schmitt, Robert C. "Density, Health, and Social Disorganization," *Journal of the American Institute of Planners*, **32**, No. 1 (1966): 38-39.

Schneider, Wolf. *Babylon Is Everywhere*. New York: McGraw-Hill,

1963.

Temko, Allan. "Reshaping Super-City: The Problem of Los Angeles," *Cry California*, **1**, No. 2 (1966):4-10.

Weismantel, William. "How the Landscape Affects Neighborhood Status," *Landscape Architecture*, **56**, No. 3 (1966):190-194.

Zisman, Sam. "Urban Open Space," in *Transactions of the North American Wildlife Conference*. Washington, D.C.: Wildlife Management Institute, in press.

CHAPTER 9

Baekeland, G. B., and P. R. Gimbel. "Para-Explorers Challenge Peru's Unknown Vilcabamba," *National Geographic*, **126**, No. 2 (1964): 268-296.

Brown, Harrison. *The Challenge of Man's Future*. New York: Viking, 1954.

Farber, Seymour. "Quality of Living—Stress and Creativity," in *Future Environments of North America*. New York: Natural History Press, 1966.

Gaymer, Roger. "Aldabra—the Case for Conserving This Coral Atoll," *Oryx*, **8**, No. 6 (1967):348-352.

McLuhan, Marshall. *Understanding Media: The Extensions of Man*. New York: McGraw-Hill Paperback, 1965.

Pacific Science Association. *Proceedings of the 11th Pacific Science Congress*. Resolutions. Mimeographed, unassembled. Tokyo, 1966.

Pan American Union. *The Cutibireni National Park: A Pilot Project in the Selva of Peru*. Washington, D.C.: Pan American Union, 1965.

Schultz, Harald. "Indians of the Amazon Darkness," *National Geographic*, **125**, No. 5 (1964):736-758.

Selye, Hans. *The Stress of Life*. New York: McGraw-Hill Paperback, 1956.

Talbot, Lee M. *A Look at Threatened Species*. London: Fauna Preservation Society, 1960.

Train, Russell. *A World Heritage Trust*. Washington, D.C.: Conservation Foundation, 1966. Mimeographed.

Weyer, Edward. *Primitive Peoples Today*. London: Hamish Hamilton, 1959.

CHAPTER 10

Chase, Stuart. "Can We Stay Prosperous?" *Saturday Review,* February 11, 1967, pp. 20-22.

Dasmann, Raymond F. *Conservation Planning on a National Scale.* Proceedings of the 11th Pacific Science Congress. Mimeographed. Tokyo, 1966.

————. *The Destruction of California.* New York: Macmillan, 1965.

Galbraith, John K. *The Affluent Society.* Boston: Houghton Mifflin, 1958.

Index

Index

271